ELEMENTARY STATISTIC[...]

CW00688676

Physical Sciences

Editor

DR R. O. DAVIES
M.SC, D.PHIL

Reader in Physics, Queen Mary College,
University of London

ELEMENTARY
STATISTICAL
MECHANICS

G. A. P. Wyllie

Senior Lecturer in Natural Philosophy
University of Glasgow

HUTCHINSON UNIVERSITY LIBRARY
LONDON

HUTCHINSON & CO (*Publishers*) LTD
178–202 Great Portland Street, London, W.1

London Melbourne Sydney
Auckland Bombay Toronto
Johannesburg New York

First published 1970

*This book has been set in Times New Roman type face.
It has been printed in Great Britain by William Clowes
and Sons Ltd, London and Beccles, on Smooth Wove
paper and bound by Wm. Brendon of Tiptree, Essex*

ISBN 0 09 101320 8 (cased)
0 09 101321 6 (paper)

CONTENTS

PREFACE

This book contains a simplified version of a lecture course delivered over several years in the University of Glasgow. In it I have adopted the standpoint of E. T. Jaynes, that statistical mechanics is concerned with making the best of situations where we must forecast the behaviour of physical systems given only partial information about their condition, using the quantitative measure of information developed by Shannon.

One or two good books based on this approach already exist. I have tried here to give a clear account of a range of important physical results while using no mathematics beyond quite elementary algebra and analysis. A few standard results in analysis and quantum theory are used although their proof requires more mathematical technique than does this book itself. These results are easy to understand and use, and this book can certainly be studied with no more than an elementary knowledge of quantum physics.

Taylor's expansion, and iteration, are the most convenient mathematical crowbars available to the working physicist for prying open problems. They appear repeatedly through the work.

I have learnt from many books and colleagues. Books by Schrödinger, Tolman and Khinchin I have found particularly important. Drs W. K. Burton and R. O. Davies have offered frequent and fruitful criticism, which I have respected, and advice, which I have occasionally accepted. Blame for the remaining errors and obscurities must be all my own.

INTRODUCTION

Thermal physics has two main divisions, one concerned with the static, equilibrium properties of matter, the other concerned with the rates of processes. In systems which are inhomogeneous in space—containing variations of temperature or concentration, for example—transport processes such as heat flow and diffusion occur: in homogeneous systems not in an equilibrium state, such as a magnetized paramagnetic substance just after the removal of the polarizing field, pure relaxation processes occur.

With increased understanding of the properties of atoms and molecules, it has become possible in the realm of statistical physics to understand the relation between the bulk properties of matter and the structure and behaviour of its atomic and molecular constituents. The term 'statistical mechanics' has by a historical accident (equilibrium theory, being easier, developed faster) been reserved for the theory of equilibrium properties, while 'rate theory' or 'kinetic theory' describes the explanation of time-dependent effects.

The prototype of statistical physics is the kinetic theory of gases, developed through the latter part of the nineteenth century, especially by Maxwell, Clausius and Boltzmann. This theory gives at an elementary level an account of the ideal gas, and an outline of transport processes in real gases, in terms of the concepts of the mean energy, and the mean free path, of gas molecules.

One of its most important results is the Maxwell–Boltzmann velocity distribution law, that the number of molecules with speeds in the range $c \rightarrow c + dc$ is proportional to $c^2 \exp(-mc^2/2kT) \, dc$, and its extension, to add potential energy to the kinetic energy in the exponent. In this expression m is the molecular mass, T the absolute temperature, and k the general constant named after Boltzmann.

One of Boltzmann's major contributions was his identification of the thermodynamic function, the entropy, with a function of the dynamical condition of the system. At the turn of the century, Willard Gibbs published a further great clarification of the whole subject of equilibrium statistical mechanics.

Two of the results of Boltzmann and Gibbs can be very simply stated by reference to quantum states. They will be derived, and used repeatedly, in the body of this book, but are worth giving here.

The Gibbs canonical distribution is defined as follows:

Let the ith energy state of a system have energy ϵ_i, and let the system be in thermal equilibrium at absolute temperature T: then the probability that the system should be found by experiment to be in a state of energy ϵ_j is to its probability of being in a state of energy ϵ_i in the ratio $\exp[(\epsilon_i - \epsilon_j)/kT]$.

More loosely, the probability that the system is in state i is proportional to $\exp(-\epsilon_i/kT)$.

Problem: (a) Is this identical with saying that the probability that the system has energy ϵ_i is proportional to $\exp(-\epsilon_i/kT)$? (b) A particular atom has one state of zero energy and three states all on the same energy level at $k \times 1500$ K. At what temperature (measured in K) are the two levels equally populated?

Boltzmann's theorem on the entropy may be stated thus:

If the probability of occupation of the ith state of a system is p_i, the entropy S of the system is given by the sum over all states

$$-k \sum_i p_i \ln p_i$$

where ln denotes the logarithm to base e.

Problem: On the (unphysical) assumption that the atom described in (b) above has only the four states cited, what is its entropy, assuming the Gibbs ratio of the p_i, at the temperature defined in (b), at $T=0$, at $T=\infty$ and at $T=-\epsilon$, where ϵ is arbitrarily small.

It is clearly probable that for a system in thermal equilibrium the function $Z = \sum_i \exp(-\epsilon_i/kT)$, which is called the canonical partition function, will have properties of interest. We shall see that it is indeed of primary importance in the theory.

A central problem in establishing the theory is to obtain the Gibbs canonical distribution. As usual in theory, several approaches are possible. The simplest, and in many ways the most sensible, is to announce that this is the primary axiom of the theory, to be postulated and not derived. The utilitarian justification of this axiom is the correspondence of the theory with classical thermodynamics.

The Gibbs distribution is so specialized in appearance that one is tempted to find simpler axioms which produce it as a theorem. In the form of Maxwell–Boltzmann distribution, it has been deduced repeatedly by dynamical arguments, all of which on careful examination reveal an assumption of randomness not noticeably simpler than the conclusion. For particular systems, it can be derived from the second law of thermodynamics, by the impossibility of a perpetual motion of the second kind.

An alternative and very attractive approach comes from the appearance of a function, closely related to Boltzmann's form for the entropy, in the theory of communication engineering. Engineers concerned with the economic problem of efficient coding of messages developed a quantitative expression for the mean information transmitted in a given class of message. This is given by $-\sum_i p_i \ln p_i$ where p_i is the probability of occurrence of the ith message in the class. The mathematical theory of communication was almost entirely originated by Shannon. Evidently in this theory 'information' is made a term of art, with a restricted meaning, just as was done with 'work' and 'energy' in the past.

As we shall see, Shannon's definition of information enables us to assess the information content of a stated set of probabilities p_i for the occurrence of distinct events E_i. This leads to a definite policy of maximum open-mindedness. Given partial information about a situation, and a demand to assess the probabilities of its distinct possible states, we are to choose that set of probabilities which adds the least arbitrary information (in Shannon's sense) to what is given.

Some cautions are perhaps needed. First of all, the information content of a message is quite independent of the importance of its contents. It measures only its surprise value relative to the other members of the class of possible messages. Second, maximum open-mindedness is not always the best policy, in a more general sense. Best accuracy in medical diagnosis is indeed obtained by suspending judgment, and treatment, till the patient dies, then conducting a really careful post-mortem. There is then, however, no prognosis. Third, the communication literature often calls 'entropy' the function which we would obtain by taking $k = -1$, or $-1/\ln 2$. The change of sign is sometimes confusing.

E. T. Jaynes, whose arguments are followed here in a simplified form, showed how an exponential distribution corresponding to that of Gibbs can be obtained from a simpler statistical question. A very useful bonus is the establishment that the form for the entropy given above is reasonable, even when the condition of the system does not correspond to a thermal equilibrium. One or two good texts, particularly the large book by Tribus, have been based on these arguments.

The present book starts with an introduction to information theory, leading to the establishment of the canonical distribution and the connection between statistical and thermodynamic functions. We then work through the statistical mechanics of a series of simple systems. These make useful structural elements in more elaborate models, approximating to the behaviour of real objects.

The grand canonical distribution is introduced at the earliest stage at which it can be used with profit. Once this step is taken, we have much more freedom of action in tackling problems with many similar particles.

The Ising problem in one dimension is discussed at some length, and this concludes the set of topics which are precisely dealt with by elementary technique.

Most many-body problems can only be approached by fairly brutal approximations even with powerful methods. Using elementary methods, however, we obtain a number of interesting results, and the lattice gas provides a tractable and useful model for gases, liquids and solid alloys. The central problem of many-body theory is to give a reasonable account of phase changes, and the discussion of ordering on lattices gives some insight even under the very simplified quasi-chemical approximation.

In the latter part of this book we are rather in the position of Stone Age tribesmen making sporadic hunting trips into forest country which can only be cleared and colonized by the technology of a more developed civilization. It may be some consolation to the reader that known exact results, giving much more physical information than we obtain in this book, almost all require mathematical technique well beyond the level of the normal undergraduate courses in physics and chemistry. The enormous literature of statistical mechanics is largely concerned with the elaboration of ideas which I have attempted to present here in a clear form, free of some of the technical difficulties which frequently obscure them.

I

INFORMATION AND THERMODYNAMICS

State and condition

The problem of statistical mechanics, which is, historically, to construct a mechanical theory reproducing the results of thermodynamics and relating thermodynamic functions to molecular properties, becomes in more general terms the question: 'Given certain partial information about the condition of a physical system, how are we to make the "best" prediction of the results of further measurements made on the system?'

The answers to a particular class of such questions turn out indeed to be equivalent to thermodynamics—to these questions we confine our attention in this book. The more general statistical mechanics which follows this approach can in fact deal with problems other than those of thermal equilibrium, but that leads to topics no longer elementary.

The state of a physical system is determined when we know its composition and the detail of its motion. By composition we mean so many particles, of such sorts, in such states of combination. Groups of particles whose mutual relation is unaltered during the whole period we are to study—stable molecules, for example—can be treated as entities of one independent type even if similar particles appear in another role elsewhere in the system.

In classical mechanics, detailed specification of the motion of a system implies a knowledge of all positions and velocities of, and the forces of interaction between, particles so that a unique set of positions and velocities is determined at any later time, given the complete set of positions and velocities at one time.

In quantum mechanics, which physical systems do in fact obey, it is meaningless to make a simultaneous specification of positions and velocities—more precisely, positions and the corresponding momenta—with arbitrarily great precision. The state of motion of a system is determined with maximum precision—as a so-called 'pure' state—by the exact prescription of the simultaneous values of as many physical variables as possible. The set of variables for a given system can, of course, be chosen in many different ways and often does not include the positions of the constituent particles; more commonly the chosen variables are the energy and various momenta, in particular the total linear momentum and angular momentum of the system.

The energy has a specially interesting role because in quantum mechanics energy and time are conjugate quantities, so that an exact statement of the energy of a system is incompatible with any statement of the time of an event involving that system: the states of the system which are constant in time are then the states of definite energy. Since we are concerned with steady (or slowly varying) conditions we find it specially convenient to use these states of definite energy, 'eigenstates' of energy in the jargon of quantum mechanics,[1] as elements in describing more general conditions of the system.

The description of such a general condition is easily visualized in terms of an ideal 'complete' experiment, to which many physical experiments indeed approximate. Suppose that many copies of the system are prepared with similar histories, so that we must accept them as being in the same condition. We then pass them through a complex spectrometer sorting them into groups possessing identical values of as extensive a set as possible of compatibly measurable quantities, so that each system in a given group has ended in the same pure state. Then the number of systems in the given group divided by the total number passed into the spectrometer measures (in the limit of large numbers) the probability that the system in the prescribed initial condition should be found in this particular pure state. The condition of the system is then described by specifying the

---

[1] It is of course historically true that statistical mechanics was developed without quantum theory and indeed long before it. Planck's discovery of the quantum of action stemmed in fact from the failure of classical statistics to account for the colour of thermal radiation. However, classical statistical mechanics is extremely hard. We shall 'base our treatment of statistical mechanics entirely on the quantum picture just outlined, and fall back on classical mechanics only as an approximation, very useful in treating a number of problems.

spectrometer—that is, a particular class of pure states—and the corresponding set of probabilities.

The condition of the system is not completely determined by the set of probabilities associated with this condition by an arbitrarily selected spectrometer. It is however true that associated with any possible condition of the system is some particular spectrometer, at least imaginable if not always practicable, determining a particular complete set of independent pure states; the condition is then completely determined by the identification of this set of states and the specification of the corresponding set of probabilities. This result is a very important but not very elementary theorem of quantum mechanics. We shall be using a special case of it, namely, that any stationary condition is determined by specifying the probabilities that a system in this condition be found in its various possible pure states corresponding to definite values of the energy.

Suppose that these energy eigenstates for a system of known constitution are arranged in order of increasing energy with energy values $\epsilon_0, \epsilon_1, \epsilon_2, \ldots, \epsilon_i, \ldots$. If any group of distinct states all correspond to the same energy value, they will be ordered within the group according to the value λ_i of some other dynamical variable compatible with the energy. Let the probability of the occurrence of the ith state be p_i. Then the expectation value of the energy of the system is given as a sum over all possible states by

$$U = \sum_i p_i \epsilon_i$$

and is fixed when we know the p's and the ϵ's.

It is interesting to ask by what criterion we should choose the set of p_i if, knowing the constitution of the system, and so the ϵ_i, we are given the value of U and asked to predict the expectation value of some other variable such as

$$L = \sum_i p_i \lambda_i$$

If some ϵ_j were just equal to U we might choose $p_j = 1$, $p_i = 0$ for all $i \neq j$, but this seems a very restricted and special choice. Evidently the most sensible choice of the p_i will be that which adds the least amount of arbitrary additional information to what information we already have.

The last sentence sounds very rational, but to make any practical use of it we require to establish a *measure* of information, at least for 'the information carried by the set of probabilities associated with an exhaustive set of mutually exclusive events'. The mutually exclusive events which interest us will of course be the appearance of the system in the various independent pure states.

Information

We now look for a reasonable way of assigning a numerical value to the information carried by the set of probabilities associated with a complete set of mutually exclusive events—the outcomes of subjecting a system to our ideal spectrometer.

Evidently, the more information that is given in the specification of the condition of the system, the less remains to be found by experiment; in an extreme case, if we know in advance that *one* outcome is certain, that is, that it has probability unity and all other outcomes have probability zero, the experiment must give this outcome and so tells us nothing new. It is therefore natural to turn first to the question of evaluating the information gained by a trial, as complementary to the information carried by the specification.

Let us consider the complete (exhaustive and mutually exclusive) set of events E_i with the assigned probabilities p_i, and suppose that on one trial the particular event E_i has occurred. This event is the more informative the less likely it was to occur, so the information increases as p_i decreases. It is hard to imagine that, with really independent events, a change in the relative probability of E_j and E_k makes any difference to the information we gain from the occurrence of E_i. Accordingly, we propose that the information gained from the one occurrence of E_i should be $I(p_i)$ where I is a monotonic decreasing function of otherwise unknown form.

To identify this function I more closely, consider the result of making two independent trials. The pairs of events E_i, E_j, which are the possible outcomes of the double trial, themselves constitute a complete set of events with probabilities p_{ij} which are equal to $p_i p_j$ since the events E_i, E_j are independent. Thus the occurrence of the particular pair of events E_i and E_j has given us information $I(p_{ij}) = I(p_i p_j)$. It would be convenient if information were so defined that this $I(p_{ij})$ were equal to the sum of the amounts of information obtained by considering the occurrence of E_i and E_j separately. (Inequality would then be the indication that E_i and E_j were not in fact independent events!) Thus we need to have

$$I(p_i p_j) = I(p_i) + I(p_j)$$

and we see that $I(p) = -c \ln p$, where c is an arbitrary positive constant (remember that $p \leqslant 1$!), fits all the requirements we have developed so far.

If then we consider a great number N of independent trials, E_i will occur Np_i times and the *average information gained per trial* is

$$\bar{I} = -c \sum_i p_i \ln p_i$$

Obviously $\bar{I}$ is zero if any $p_i = 1$ (all the other p_j are then zero). Let M be the number of possible outcomes E_i. We have

$$\sum p_i = 1$$

so for any permissible set of variations dp_i of the p_i we must have

$$\sum dp_i = 0$$

Now
$$\frac{\partial \bar{I}}{\partial p_i} = -c(1 + \ln p_i)$$

so the variation of $\bar{I}$ corresponding to the set of variations dp_i of its arguments is

$$d\bar{I} = -c \sum (1 + \ln p_i)\, dp_i$$

If any particular set of p_i correspond to a turning value of $\bar{I}$, then $d\bar{I}$ is zero for dp_i starting at this point, so the condition for a turning value of $\bar{I}$ is

$$\sum (1 + \ln p_i)\, dp_i = 0$$

subject to a, $\sum dp_i = 0$, which is evidently equivalent to, b, $\sum \ln p_i\, dp_i = 0$, subject to the same auxiliary condition.

The neat way to resolve this is by Lagrange's method. If α is a constant (to be determined immediately) the relation

$$\sum \ln p_i\, dp_i + \alpha \sum dp_i = 0$$

i.e.
$$\sum (\ln p_i + \alpha)\, dp_i = 0$$

follows from a and b. Suppose α is $-\ln p_1$, whatever this may turn out to be. For this value of α, the coefficient of dp_1 is identically zero, so the other dp_i may now be any imaginable set of variations. The fact that dp_1 is 'minus their sum' drops out of the equations, and all the coefficients of the independent dp_i must now vanish. We see then that a turning value of $\bar{I}$ occurs when all the p_i are equal and of value $\exp(-\alpha)$. The value of α is determined by looking back at the completeness equation

$$\sum p_i = 1$$

so $\bar{I}$ has its turning point when each $p_i = M^{-1}$. It is easily verified that this gives a maximum, and

$$\bar{I}_{max} = -c \sum \frac{1}{M} \ln \frac{1}{M}$$
$$= c \ln M$$

The most natural choice for the information *carried by the set of probabilities* p_i would then seem to be

$$H(p_1, \ldots, p_i, \ldots) = \bar{I}_{max} - \bar{I}(p_1, \ldots, p_i, \ldots)$$

taking the situation of perfect ignorance, in which all the alternatives seem equally likely, as the reference situation.

However, we shall find ourselves dealing with a class of problems in which M is infinite, although the class of distributions p_i will always be such as to make $\bar{I}(p_1, \ldots, p_i, \ldots)$ finite. To avoid having infinite constant terms in our mathematics, we then choose the situation of perfect certainty, in which any one $p_i = 1$, as reference situation, so that the measure of the information[1] carried by a set of probabilities p_i is

$$H(p_1, \ldots, p_i, \ldots) = \sum_i p_i \ln p_i$$

where we have taken the arbitrary constant $c = 1$.

'*Least information*' *prescription*: In sum, then, when given partial information about a system which is to be described by a discrete set of probabilities p_i, we choose that set of p_i which makes the sum $\sum_i p_i \ln p_i$ a minimum without becoming inconsistent with the information supplied.

The canonical distribution

Accepting the measure of information developed in the last section, we find that the problem posed at the end of the previous section is in

---

[1] We have now shown that the function H defined above gives a convenient measure of information. It is not obvious that no other measure is conveniently possible. The proof of this has been subjected to a great deal of refinement by the professional mathematicians. There is an excellent account in Khinchin (1957), and a more economical but rather harder discussion, due to Fadiev, in Feinstein's book (1958). Both these discussions require a certain amount of mathematical sophistication from the reader: Feinstein, A., *Foundations of information theory* (McGraw-Hill, 1958); Khinchin, A. I., *Mathematical foundations of information theory* (Dover, 1957).

sufficiently definite terms to be solved. It now runs as follows. Given
a set of states with energy levels ϵ_i, and an expected energy

$$U = \sum_i p_i \epsilon_i$$

where $$\sum_i p_i = 1, \quad \text{all } p_i \geqslant 0$$

to determine the p_i so that $\sum_i p_i \ln p_i$ is a minimum.

The neatest procedure is again that of Lagrange. A variation $\mathrm{d}p_i$
of each probability away from the desired value gives

$$\sum_i (1 + \ln p_i)\, \mathrm{d}p_i = 0$$

$$\sum_i \mathrm{d}p_i = 0$$

$$\sum_i \epsilon_i\, \mathrm{d}p_i = 0$$

so for some constant γ, β we have

$$\sum_i (1 + \gamma + \ln p_i + \beta\epsilon_i)\, \mathrm{d}p_i = 0$$

where the $\mathrm{d}p_i$ may now be considered as completely independent
variations, so that

$$p_i = \mathrm{e}^{-(1+\gamma)}\, \mathrm{e}^{-\beta\epsilon_i}$$

$$= \frac{\mathrm{e}^{-\beta\epsilon_i}}{\sum_i \mathrm{e}^{-\beta\epsilon_i}}, \quad \text{since } \sum p_i = 1.$$

This corresponds closely to the canonical distribution introduced by
Willard Gibbs.

The constant β is to be determined from the relation

$$U = \sum p_i \epsilon_i$$

$$= \sum \frac{\epsilon_i\, \mathrm{e}^{-\beta\epsilon_i}}{\sum \mathrm{e}^{-\beta\epsilon_i}}$$

$$= -\frac{\partial}{\partial\beta}\left[\ln\left(\sum \mathrm{e}^{-\beta\epsilon_i}\right)\right]$$

This is in general a very intractable equation to solve for β, given U.
We shall see that by good luck our physical problems can be presented in such a form that we first state the value of β and then
construct U.

We see moreover that

$$p_i = \frac{e^{-\beta\epsilon_i}}{\sum e^{-\beta\epsilon_i}}$$

$$= -\frac{1}{\beta}\frac{\partial}{\partial\epsilon_i}\left[\ln\left(\sum e^{-\beta\epsilon_i}\right)\right]$$

so that all the properties of the system, in a condition specified by this set of p_i for the energy eigenstates, can be predicted if we know the function

$$Z \equiv \sum e^{-\beta\epsilon_i}$$

as a function of β and the ϵ_i. This function Z is called the partition function for the system

At first sight Z is a function of many, perhaps infinitely many, variables, and it is not obvious that it is going to be much use to us. However, in the physically interesting cases, all the ϵ are determined as functions of relatively few parameters, e.g. the volume available to the system and the constants determining its internal interaction, and once Z is expressed as a function of these parameters and of β our problem is very much simplified.

In order to see the full beauty of the subject, we must now establish the connection between the pure statistical mechanics we have just been discussing and the rules of classical thermodynamics. First of all, we note one or two further properties of p_i and U.

For given β, p_i decreases as ϵ_i increases: the system is more likely to be in its ground state than any other single state, however large U may be.

Again, given the set of ϵ_i,

$$\frac{\partial U}{\partial\beta} = \frac{\partial}{\partial\beta}\left(-Z^{-1}\frac{\partial Z}{\partial\beta}\right)$$

$$= \frac{1}{Z^2}\left[\left(\sum \epsilon_i e^{-\beta\epsilon_i}\right)^2 - \left(\sum e^{-\beta\epsilon_i}\right)\left(\sum \epsilon_i^2 e^{-\beta\epsilon_i}\right)\right]$$

$$= \left(\sum \epsilon_i p_i\right)^2 - \sum \epsilon_i^2 p_i$$

$$= \langle\epsilon\rangle^2 - \langle\epsilon^2\rangle$$

$$= -\langle(\epsilon - \langle\epsilon\rangle)^2\rangle$$

$$< 0$$

since the expectation value of the square of a real quantity is necessarily positive, where $\langle x\rangle \equiv \sum x_i p_i$ is the expectation value of any function x depending on the energy levels. Thus U is a monotonic decreasing function of β. (Evidently, $\langle \epsilon \rangle$ is U.)

Notions of thermodynamics

Classical thermodynamics is a theory of the equilibrium states of physical systems; it gives a criterion for the direction in which a given system will move towards equilibrium, but says nothing about the rate of this movement.

Two physical systems can interact in a variety of ways; in particular, they may exchange energy or matter with each other. For the present, we consider situations in which they exchange energy alone. This may take place either by the transfer of radiation, or by mechanical interaction at an interface. We idealize from experience to the notion that two systems which would otherwise interpenetrate and mix may be separated by a partition which transfers energy from one side to another, but is impenetrable to material particles. A practical approximation to a partition of this sort is a thin conducting metal sheet. A model of such a partition might be a perfectly elastic membrane[1] which permitted particles on either side to exchange mechanical energy, by simultaneous collision with the membrane, without allowing them to pass through.

If two systems are thus allowed to exchange energy and left to age, we find that they settle to an equilibrium condition, which we take as defining thermal equilibrium. We then discover that, given systems A, B and C, if A is in thermal equilibrium with B, and is then found to be in thermal equilibrium with C (that is, undergoes no change of condition on equilibrating with C, as just described), B will be found to be in thermal equilibrium with C. Thus systems in thermal equilibrium with each other share a common property, which we call temperature, and an empirical scale of temperature can be constructed (as, for example, in the ordinary mercury thermometer) in terms of some convenient measurable property such as the relative density of mercury and glass at nearly constant pressure.

Calorimetric experiments then lead one to the idea of a quantity, calorimetric heat, which is apparently conserved in an enclosed system which is not the seat of a chemical reaction and does not

---

[1] One can imagine such a membrane so light and stiff that a quantum of energy at its lowest frequency of natural vibration would be much larger than the thermal energy per degree of freedom in the systems. The heat capacity of the membrane itself could thus be as small as one wished. See the later discussion of the ideal insulating crystal (pp. 34–38), and especially the conclusion about the specific heat at very low temperatures.

have substantial amounts of work done on it. The unit of calorimetric heat is the calorie. The equivalence of heat and energy, which we have presupposed in some of the foregoing remarks, is then established by the universally constant ratio of energy lost to heat gained in all sorts of dissipative processes.

We are thus led to the idea of the 'internal energy' of a system, which one might define as the sum of its heat energy and of the energy it possesses as a result of its macroscopic interactions with fields of stress, or of electric or gravitational force, and so on. The same idea can be reached, however, in a rather more subtle and satisfying way, as follows.

Consider a system isolated by non-conducting partitions so that it cannot exchange heat with its surroundings, but suppose that work can be done on it, either mechanically, by displacing its boundaries, or electrically. If we now take any two states of internal thermal equilibrium of the system, it is possible to pass from one to the other (but *not* in general in the reverse direction) by performing work on the system in a variety of different ways. For example, if we deal with a simple fluid the thermal equilibrium state is defined by volume and temperature. Then to pass from one state to another, we may raise the temperature by violent stirring at the initial volume, drop the volume instantaneously to its final value at any suitable moment, and stir on to the final temperature, or combine stirring with volume variation in any arbitrary way. In whatever way an 'adiabatic' process of this sort is carried out, we find that the total work done in bringing the system from a given initial state to a given final state is the same. This is one statement of the first law of thermodynamics: the work done in the adiabatic transition then *defines* the difference in internal energy of final and initial states.

There will be possible processes which are not adiabatic, connecting the same two states. If the increase of internal energy in the process is ΔU and the work done on the system[1] in one such process is $-W$, we *define* the heat Q supplied to the system by the relation

$$Q = \Delta U + W$$

We thus have a thermodynamic definition of heat which is completely independent of calorimetry.

Now consider the special (impracticable) class of processes in

---

[1] That is, the work done by the system is W. The standard choice of sign reflects the preoccupation of the men who invented thermodynamics with heat engines.

which the system passes through a sequence of equilibrium states. In such processes, called quasi-static, there would be no dissipation of energy within the system; and these processes may, unlike the general dissipative process, take place in the reverse direction. For the theory of heat engines, a special interest attaches to the cyclic quasi-static processes, in which the system returns to its initial state.

By arguments which are best studied at length in books devoted to thermodynamics, one can establish, either by a consideration of reversible cycles or, more directly but with more difficulty, from the fact that arbitrarily close to a given equilibrium state of a system lie equilibrium states inaccessible from the given state by any adiabatic process, the existence of the quantities called entropy and absolute temperature.

The differential relation for a small quasi-static transition,

$$\mathrm{d}Q = \mathrm{d}U + \mathrm{d}W$$

possesses an integrating factor T^{-1} such that

$$\mathrm{d}S = T^{-1}\,\mathrm{d}Q = T^{-1}(\mathrm{d}U + \mathrm{d}W)$$

defines a function S of the state of the system, called the entropy. The integrating quotient T is called the absolute temperature, and is easily shown to coincide with the temperature that would be indicated by an ideal gas thermometer. Its most striking property is the existence of a physically meaningful 'absolute zero' of temperature.

The existence of the integrating factor is trivial for a simple fluid, with only two thermodynamic degrees of freedom. This fact is often responsible for the suspicion felt by elementary students that thermodynamics is an empty subject. The result is *not* trivial for any more complex system, and the existence of a definite T for any equilibrium situation is what makes thermodynamics possible and useful.

The connection of statistics with thermodynamics
To establish this connection we concentrate on the following ideas.

(i) The internal energy of a system plays a fundamental role in thermodynamics.

(ii) Equilibrium between two systems is an easier notion to lay hold of than equilibrium within one.

(iii) The absolute temperature appears as an integrating quotient in the heat–work relation.

We enquire now whether a system whose condition is as broadly specified as possible, subject to the condition that the expectation value U_S of its energy is known, can be identified as a system in thermal equilibrium, and, if so, how U_S and β are related to the thermodynamic variables.

First of all, if the dispersion of the energy is small, that is,

$$\frac{\partial U_S}{\partial \beta} \ll U_S^2$$

so that values of energy much different from U_S are unlikely to be found, we will be content to identify U_S with the thermodynamic internal energy U.

Let us suppose provisionally that this identification can be made in general.

Now consider two distinct physical systems (1) and (2), with states of energy $\alpha_{1,i}$, $\alpha_{2,j}$ respectively, and suppose first of all that the expectation energies U_1, U_2 of these systems are separately specified.

Then the probability that system (1) is in its ith state is

$$p_{1,i} = e^{-\beta_1 \alpha_{1,i}} / Z_1(\beta_1)$$

where

$$Z_1(\beta_1) = \sum_i e^{-\beta_1 \alpha_{1,i}}$$

and moreover

$$U_1 = \sum_i p_{1,i} \alpha_{1,i}$$

Similarly the probability that system (2) is in its jth state is

$$p_{2,j} = e^{-\beta_2 \alpha_{2,j}} / Z_2(\beta_2)$$

where

$$Z_2(\beta_2) = \sum_j e^{-\beta_2 \alpha_{2,j}}$$

and moreover

$$U_2 = \sum_j p_{2,j} \alpha_{2,j}$$

We now think of these two systems as the separate parts of a single joint system whose levels are $\alpha_{i,j} = \alpha_{1,i} + \alpha_{2,j}$ and whose states are enumerated by taking all possible values for the pair of indices i, j. The probability that the joint system is in the state i, j is now

$$p_{i,j} = e^{-(\beta_1 \alpha_{1,i} + \beta_2 \alpha_{2,j})} / Z_1(\beta_1) Z_2(\beta_2)$$

Alternatively, consider the situation where we only specify a total expectation energy U for the joint system whose states i, j have energy levels α_{ij}. Then we must have

$$p_{i,j} = e^{-\beta \alpha_{ij}} / Z(\beta)$$

where
$$Z(\beta) = \sum_{i,j} e^{-\beta\alpha_{ij}}$$
$$= \sum_i \sum_j e^{-\beta(\alpha_{1,i}+\alpha_{2,j})}$$
$$= \left(\sum_i e^{-\beta\alpha_{1,i}}\right)\left(\sum_j e^{-\beta\alpha_{2,j}}\right)$$
$$= Z_1(\beta)Z_2(\beta)$$

and β is determined by
$$U = \sum_{i,j} p_{i,j}\alpha_{ij}$$

This last sum can be separated as
$$\frac{1}{Z(\beta)}\left\{\left(\sum_i \alpha_{1,i}\,e^{-\beta\alpha_{1,i}}\right)\left(\sum_j e^{-\beta\alpha_{2,j}}\right) + \left(\sum_i e^{-\beta\alpha_{1,i}}\right)\left(\sum_j \alpha_{2,j}\,e^{-\beta\alpha_{2,j}}\right)\right\}$$
$$= \frac{1}{Z(\beta)}\left\{U_1(\beta)Z_1(\beta)\cdot Z_2(\beta)+Z_1(\beta)\cdot U_2(\beta)Z_2(\beta)\right\}$$
$$= U_1(\beta)+U_2(\beta)$$

We now compare this with the situation resulting when the two systems are joined not merely conceptually but also physically, to the extent that although the energy levels α_i and α_j are not disturbed by the interaction, energy may nevertheless be exchanged between the systems. In such a connection total energy is conserved, so we must set $U = U_1(\beta_1)+U_2(\beta_2)$.

We observe first of all that if $\beta_1 = \beta_2$, then on bringing the systems into contact there is no change in the condition of either of them. Thus equality of β is equivalent to equality of temperature. Moreover, since U_1, U_2 and U are monotonic decreasing functions of β, we have the situation illustrated, for unequal β_1 and β_2, where β_1, β_2 may be interchanged, but β must always lie between them. Since

$$U(\beta) = U_1(\beta)+U_2(\beta)$$
$$= U_1(\beta_1)+U_2(\beta_2)$$

the system which begins with the lower value of β will decrease its U value as it equilibrates with the other; that is, the system with the lower β will give up energy to the other, so that the lower β corresponds to higher temperature.

Thus, β is so far identified as an inverse measure of temperature, the same β value corresponding to the same temperature no matter what the nature of the particular physical systems we are considering.

The next step is to see whether quantities corresponding to heat

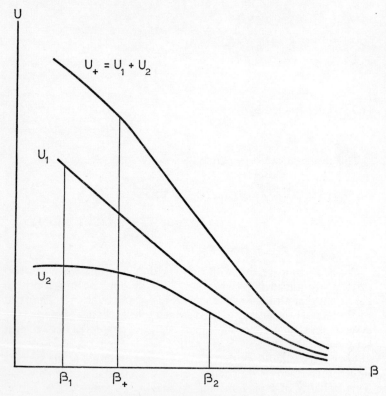

Fig. 1. U, β relations for systems 1 and 2 and for their union. [β_+ is defined by $U_1(\beta_1) + U_2(\beta_2) = U_+(\beta_+)$].

and work can be picked out in the statistical theory. In thermodynamic language, we already know that increase in internal energy is equal to heat supplied less work done, that is,

$$dU = dQ - dW$$

Again, from the statistical expression,

$$U = \sum p_i \epsilon_i$$
$$dU = \sum \epsilon_i \, dp_i + \sum p_i \, d\epsilon_i$$

It would be very agreeable if we could identify these quantities just as they stand. This will now be justified.

To see which terms correspond to external work, we recall that real processes approximate better to quasi-static processes the more slowly they proceed. Suppose that the system is manipulated by applying an external force field which varies very slowly with time. It follows from quantum theory that a varying field can produce transitions between two levels only so far as its time dependence contains the frequency ν, such that $h\nu$ is equal to the difference in energy of the levels. Thus if the force varies slowly enough it will produce as few transitions as we please, so that its effect is entirely in changing the ϵ_i, without producing any change in the p_i.[1] Then $\sum p_i \, d\epsilon_i$ is the expectation value of the change in U produced by such a force, and can be identified as the work done *on* the system, which is $-dW$. In consequence, $\sum_i \epsilon_i \, dp_i$ must be identified as dQ.

The quantity β is already identified as an empirical temperature. To complete the discussion we must find what function of β serves as an integrating factor for dQ, which will lead us to the absolute temperature and the entropy.

This argument can be short-circuited by asking instead whether the information function H has a thermodynamic meaning. We have

$$H = \sum_i p_i \ln p_i$$

so for any variation of the p_i

$$dH = \sum \ln p_i \, dp_i + \sum dp_i$$

and since $p_i = Z^{-1} e^{-\beta \epsilon_i}$

$$dH = -\sum \beta \epsilon_i \, dp_i + \sum (1 - \ln Z) \, dp_i$$
$$= -\beta \sum \epsilon_i \, dp_i + (1 - \ln Z) \sum dp_i$$

Now $\sum p_i = 1$, so $\sum dp_i = 0$, and we have simply

$$dH = -\beta \, dQ$$

[1] The critical reader will be worried at this stage for at least one good reason. An applied force which changes the ϵ_i without altering the p_i will in general bring the system into a condition which is not one of thermal equilibrium. Unless all the energy levels change by the same fraction, the p_i cannot be expressed in terms of the new ϵ_i by a single new value of β. We can of course save the argument in an elementary way by postulating that our ideal applied forces do change all energy levels in the same proportion—which is true if the frequencies of all oscillators in the system change in the same proportion: but we must recognize that in several experimental situations one produces different thermal regimes in different characteristic motions of the same system. Such situations are not in thermal equilibrium. See pp. 32 and 34.

Obviously H is a single-valued function of the condition of the system, so β is itself an integrating factor of dQ. Since we know that

$$dS = T^{-1} \, dQ$$

any other integrating factor such as β must have the form

$$\beta = T^{-1} f(S)$$

We have already seen that β is a measure of temperature, independent of the nature, and in particular of the size, of the system, whereas S is (like H) an extensive quantity, such that if we consider two systems A and B conceptually united, the entropy of the joint system is just $S_A + S_B$, the sum of the separate entropies. Thus $f(S)$ can only be a constant, whose numerical value depends simply on our choice of a system of units, and it is conventional to write

$$\beta = \frac{1}{kT}$$

and

$$S = -k \sum p_i \ln p_i$$

where k is called Boltzmann's constant.

In sum, then, there is a complete correspondence between the broadest description of a system of which we know nothing except the expectation value of its energy, and the thermodynamic description of the system with the same value assigned to its internal energy.

Again, substituting $p_i = e^{-\beta \epsilon_i}/Z$ into the expression for S we obtain

$$
\begin{aligned}
S &= -k \sum p \ln p \\
&= k \left[\sum \beta \epsilon \frac{e^{-\beta \epsilon}}{Z} + \sum \frac{e^{-\beta \epsilon}}{Z} \ln Z \right] \\
&= k[\beta U + \ln Z] \\
&= \frac{U}{T} + k \ln Z
\end{aligned}
$$

or; the Helmholtz free energy F is given by

$$F \equiv U - TS = -kT \ln Z$$

Fluctuations

In the elementary thermodynamics of large systems, one normally thinks of the internal energy as constant whether the system is in contact with a heat bath—that is, a second system at the same temperature, of large thermal capacity—or strictly isolated. Observation of a small system such as a Brownian particle, or the moving part of a sensitive galvanometer, shows that in thermal equilibrium such a system is continually fluctuating in energy as it gains or loses it in interaction with its surroundings. The statistical description we have chosen to employ is strictly suitable to describe a system interacting with a heat bath, and so at a constant temperature and not at a constant energy. For large systems, the fluctuation of energy is usually so small compared to the mean energy that the distinction need not be drawn: but for a system consisting of a liquid in equilibrium with its vapour at the saturation vapour pressure, to take one example, large fluctuations can and will occur. That particular situation is not covered by the model we have used so far, which corresponds to a system at constant volume. Since the whole thermodynamics of a system is implied by its thermodynamics at constant volume, so long as that volume appears explicitly in the thermodynamic functions, this limitation is not one of principle. We shall later introduce a powerful method which covers such more general situations with no increase of effort. It must however be emphasized that all of thermodynamics is implied by the results we already have.

Conclusion

The statistical description of a system by the set of probabilities

$$p_i = Z^{-1} e^{-\epsilon_i/kT}$$

where

$$Z = \sum_i e^{-\epsilon_i/kT}$$

corresponds exactly to the canonical distribution of Willard Gibbs. If one is only concerned with equilibrium thermodynamics, the statistical mechanics can perfectly well be founded by postulating this distribution law. The introductory argument which we have worked through has two merits. First, it lends plausibility to what at first appears a highly arbitrary distribution, though this plausibility can be established by arguments from kinetic theory, and was historically so established; secondly, it gives a guide on how to proceed when discussing situations, other than those of thermal equilibrium, where irreversible processes are advancing at a finite rate. The problem of the rates of real processes, however, lies beyond the scope of this book.

2

THE STATISTICS OF
SOME SIMPLE SYSTEMS

In this chapter we shall consider the application of the canonical distribution to find the thermodynamical behaviour of some very simple physical systems whose energy levels are easily identified. This will help to emphasize that the statistical method is applicable to all physical systems, regardless of size, which are in a condition correctly described by specifying a temperature. It is true that statistical mechanics was originally developed as a theory of large and complicated systems, but this restriction is no longer necessary.

The Fermi oscillator
This simplest of all ideal physical systems possesses only two distinct states, with energies 0 and ϵ, say. The partition function is

$$Z = 1 + e^{-\epsilon/kT}$$

and the probability of the occupation of the ground state is

$$p_0 = \frac{1}{1 + e^{-\epsilon/kT}}$$

and of the excited state is

$$p_1 = \frac{e^{-\epsilon/kT}}{1 + e^{-\epsilon/kT}} = \frac{1}{1 + e^{\epsilon/kT}}$$

while

$$U = \epsilon p_1 = \frac{\epsilon}{1 + e^{\epsilon/kT}}$$

The real system most directly analogous to the Fermi oscillator is a particle of spin $\frac{1}{2}$ (i.e. with intrinsic angular momentum $\hbar/2$) and magnetic moment μ, in a magnetic field H. Such particles include electrons, protons and various atomic nuclei. In the presence of the field, the eigenstates of energy of this particle are the states in which the angular momentum, and with it the magnetic moment, is either parallel or anti-parallel to the field, giving values of the magnetic energy $-\mu H$ and $+\mu H$ relative to the cross orientation. With this symmetric disposition of the energy values we get a slightly different appearance of the formulae.

$$Z = e^{\mu H/kT} + e^{-\mu H/kT}$$
$$= 2 \cosh (\mu H/kT)$$
$$p_0 = e^{\mu H/kT}/Z = (1 + e^{-2\mu H/kT})^{-1}$$
$$p_1 = e^{-\mu H/kT}/Z = (1 + e^{2\mu H/kT})^{-1}$$

and

$$U = -\mu H p_0 + \mu H p_1$$
$$= -\mu H \frac{e^{\mu H/kT} - e^{-\mu H/kT}}{e^{\mu H/kT} + e^{-\mu H/kT}}$$
$$= -\mu H \tanh (\mu H/kT)$$

The expectation value of the magnetization in the direction of the field

$$m = \mu p_0 - \mu p_1$$
$$= \mu \tanh (\mu H/kT)$$

If $\mu H \ll kT$, then

$$m = \mu^2 H/kT$$
$$= \chi_a H$$

where χ_a is the susceptibility per particle, so

$$\chi_a = \mu^2/kT$$

Again, the free energy per particle is

$$F = -kT \ln Z$$
$$= -kT \ln 2 - kT \ln \cosh (\mu H/kT)$$

so that the change in free energy associated with the field is

$$\Delta F = -kT \ln \cosh (\mu H/kT)$$

and for the usual situation with $\mu H \ll kT$,

$$\cosh (\mu H/kT) \sim 1 + \tfrac{1}{2}(\mu H/kT)^2$$

so

$$\Delta F = -\frac{1}{2}\frac{\mu^2 H^2}{kT} = \frac{1}{2}U$$

The $-kT\ln 2$ in F deserves note. It arises from a permanent entropy of $k\ln 2$ due to the presence of two equally probable states when there is no field, that is to say, from a double degeneracy of the ground state in the absence of a field. We note also that $\Delta F = -\frac{1}{2}Hm$ is just the usual estimate in magnetic theory for the energy associated with the induced magnetization m.

A different use for the idea of the Fermi oscillator will arise when we are considering systems of many particles, so need only be noted briefly at this point. Suppose that we are concerned with a system containing a number of similar particles which obey Pauli's exclusion principle, and that we have a set of suitable independent states to describe the motion of the single particles. Then a state of the whole system is completely defined when we state which of the one-particle states are occupied. Provided we can associate a definite energy with each one-particle state (this takes a good deal of arranging for strongly interacting particles), then since any such state is either unoccupied, or occupied by at most one particle, it can be regarded as having a Fermi oscillator associated with its state of occupation. We shall make more use of this idea later.

The harmonic (Bose) oscillator

We take from quantum mechanics the result that the energy levels of a harmonic oscillator, measured from the value of the potential energy at the centre, are at $(n+\frac{1}{2})h\nu$, where n is any positive integer or zero, and ν is the frequency of the oscillator. For an oscillator in one dimension, or with one degree of freedom, the levels are single, that is, with only one distinct state at each energy level, so the partition function is

$$\begin{aligned}
Z &= \sum_{n=0}^{\infty} e^{-(n+\frac{1}{2})h\nu/kT} \\
&= \frac{e^{-\frac{1}{2}h\nu/kT}}{1-e^{-h\nu/kT}}
\end{aligned}$$

The probability of the nth excited state is

$$\begin{aligned}
p_n &= e^{-(n+\frac{1}{2})h\nu/kT}/Z \\
&= e^{-nh\nu/kT}(1-e^{-h\nu/kT})
\end{aligned}$$

Thus $$U = \sum_{n=0}^{\infty} p_n(n+\frac{1}{2})h\nu$$

and it is a simple exercise to reduce this to

$$U = \frac{h\nu}{2} + \frac{h\nu}{e^{h\nu/kT} - 1}$$

if one remembers that

$$\sum n\, e^{-nx} = -\frac{d}{dx} \sum e^{-nx}$$

The easiest way to obtain the entropy is not by hammering out $\sum p \ln p$ but by observing that since

$$U - TS \equiv F = -kT \ln Z,$$
$$S = k \ln Z + U/T.$$

These expressions can be simplified at extreme temperatures. In particular, if $h\nu \ll kT$, we can expand the exponential in the denominator in U and find $U \sim kT +$ powers of $h\nu/kT$ (the temperature independent term in fact cancels out exactly); while, if $h\nu \gg kT$, only the first excited state contributes appreciably, and we have

$$U \sim \frac{h\nu}{2} + h\nu\, e^{-h\nu/kT}$$

Thus at high temperatures, the specific heat C, which is $\partial U/\partial T$, has the constant value k given by the empirical rule of equipartition of energy, whereas at low temperatures the specific heat drops exponentially with $1/T$. The exponential of course goes to zero so fast, as T decreases, that it kills the infinity in C which would otherwise arise (from the T^{-2} factor which appears on taking the derivative).

Again, these results turn out to have a direct application to the many-body problem. If the particles constituting a many-body system have zero or integral spin, they are of Bose type and any number of them may appear in the same one-particle state. The energy spectrum associated with that state has thus the same intervals as an oscillator spectrum. (According to convenience, one either uses the same expressions as we have just derived, or cuts out the factor $e^{-h\nu/2kT}$ in Z and the added $h\nu/2$ in U.)

The rotor with two degrees of freedom

The rotation of, for example, a diatomic molecule consisting of two different atoms, has a fairly simple description in quantum theory. In classical mechanics, such a pair of point particles has an angular position fixed by a polar angle and an azimuth angle, and in free rotation a corresponding pair of angular momenta are constant. In quantum mechanics, the total angular momentum is fixed by a quantum number j, and the motion is determined by j, together with the angular momentum about a specified axis. These are connected by the fact that for given j, the maximum value which the component angular momentum can assume is $j\hbar$.

Since, however, the component angular momenta about different axes are not mutually compatible observables, the transverse angular momenta have zero expectation value but non-zero dispersion in such a state, so that the expectation value of the square of the total angular momentum works out at $j(j+1)\hbar^2$ instead of the $j^2\hbar^2$ one might have expected. The corresponding energy of rotation is then

$$\frac{\hbar^2}{2A} j(j+1)$$

where A, the moment of inertia of the molecule about its mass centre, is equal to $m_1 m_2 r_0^2 / (m_1 + m_2)$ for atoms of masses m_1, m_2 at separation r_0.

The number of states with this energy is the number of distinct values of the component angular momentum from $j\hbar$ to $-j\hbar$ at intervals of $\hbar$, which is $2j+1$. Thus the energy levels of the rotor are

$$\epsilon_j = \frac{\hbar^2}{2A} j(j+1)$$

with degeneracy $2j+1$. Then

$$Z = \sum_0^\infty (2j+1)\, e^{-j(j+1)\theta/T}$$

where we have introduced for convenience a characteristic temperature $\theta = \hbar^2/2Ak$. Setting further $\lambda = j + \frac{1}{2}$ we have

$$Z = \sum_{1/2}^\infty 2\lambda\, e^{-(\lambda^2 - \frac{1}{4})\theta/T}$$

Again, this expression is tractable at extreme temperatures. At very high temperature, that is, for $T \gg \theta$, the series contains many terms which contribute appreciably to its sum, and is quite accurately equivalent to the integral

$$Z \sim \int_0^\infty 2\lambda\, e^{-(\theta/T)\lambda^2}\, d\lambda$$

$$= \frac{T}{\theta}$$

Then $U = kT$—equipartition as for the oscillator.

At low temperature only the first few terms of the various series contribute. Thus we have

$$Z = 1 + 3e^{-2\theta/T} + 5e^{-6\theta/T} + \cdots$$

$$U = k\theta\left(\frac{6e^{-2\theta/T} + 30e^{-6\theta/T} + \cdots}{1 + 3e^{-2\theta/T} + \cdots}\right)$$

$$= k\theta(6e^{-2\theta/T} - 18e^{-4\theta/T} - \cdots)$$

and

$$C = k\left(\frac{\theta}{T}\right)^2 (12e^{-2\theta/T} - 72e^{-4\theta/T} - \cdots)$$

where U is most easily obtained by direct construction from the p_j and C is again $\partial U/\partial T$.

If our molecule consists of two atoms with identical nuclei there is a complication, since some states of rotation of the molecule may not occur. This is considered later on.

An ideal rubber

Since we have been concerned so far with sums over energy levels, it is amusing to digress on a system whose energy levels are all zero and whose behaviour is determined wholly by its entropy. The familiar fact that rubber under given tension shrinks when warmed indicates that a good deal of the elastic free energy stored in the stretched rubber is associated with an entropy term. The entropy is known to arise from the vast number of different configurations of nearly equal energy into which the long chain molecules of the rubber can coil themselves.

To obtain a simple calculation, we idealize ruthlessly from three dimensions to one, and from real atoms occupying space to atoms which are merely the pivot points of rigid links. A rubber molecule is viewed as a chain, rather like a surveyor's chain, laid along a straight line of length La with a certain number of segments turned backwards. Suppose there are N links, of length a, and let n be the number of those arrangements of the links which give the same total length La. Then

$$Z = n$$
$$F = -kT \ln n$$
$$U = 0$$
$$S = k \ln n$$

To evaluate n, note that the total number of links pointing forward is $\frac{1}{2}(N+L)$ and the total number of backward links is $\frac{1}{2}(N-L)$. The corresponding number of distinct sequences of forward and backward links is found by considering the links as a set of distinct objects, and evaluating the number of ways of choosing $\frac{1}{2}(N+L)$ out of N. Thus

$$n = \frac{N!}{[(N+L)/2]![(N-L)/2]!}$$

To find its logarithm we apply Stirling's theorem, which gives the first terms of the asymptotic expansion

$$\ln (N!) = (N+\tfrac{1}{2}) \ln N - N + \tfrac{1}{2} \ln (2\pi) + O(N^{-1})$$

If N and $\frac{1}{2}(N-L)$ are both large, we may neglect the terms of lower order than N, so

$$S/k = \ln n \sim N \ln N - \left[\frac{N+L}{2} \ln \frac{N+L}{2} + \frac{N-L}{2} \ln \frac{N-L}{2}\right]$$

$$= \frac{N+L}{2} \ln \frac{2N}{N+L} + \frac{N-L}{2} \ln \frac{2N}{N-L}$$

$$= -N[x \ln x + (1-x) \ln (1-x)]$$

where $x = (N+L)/2N$ and

$$F = -TS = NkT[x \ln x + (1-x) \ln (1-x)]$$

The tension P in the chain is then the derivative of free energy with respect to length, so

$$P = \frac{\partial F}{\partial (La)} = -\frac{T}{a} \frac{\partial S}{\partial L}$$

$$= NkT \frac{1}{2Na} \frac{\mathrm{d}}{\mathrm{d}x} [x \ln x + (1-x) \ln (1-x)]$$

$$= \frac{kT}{2a} \ln \frac{x}{1-x}$$

$$= \frac{kT}{2a} \ln \frac{N+L}{N-L}$$

If now we consider $L \ll N$, we have

$$\frac{N+L}{N-L} \doteqdot 1 + 2L/N$$

so

$$P = \frac{kT}{a} \cdot \frac{L}{N}$$

giving elastic behaviour at constant T, with elastic constant kT/Na^2 (since length $=La$), proportional to T and inversely to N.

Considering the brutality of the model, this is not too unlike the behaviour of actual rubbers. It may seem odd that we get a tension out of a system which has no mechanical properties, but this is less surprising if we think of the kinetics of the model in more than the one dimension. The essential property of the chain is that the links themselves are inextensible, but this means that the molecules of the heat bath, knocking the links sideways in the exchange of thermal energy, produce lengthways tension in the chain. This process is much the same as the increase in the tension of a clothes-rope at every blow of a carpet-beater. The great power of statistical thermodynamics is that we can find the average tension (but not its rate of fluctuation) without the long and difficult consideration of a detailed kinetic model.

One particle in a box

The real walls confining the particle are replaced by an equivalent potential field. No generality is lost, so long as we consider volume rather than surface effects, if we take the box as a cubical region of edge a in which the potential energy is constant, and can be taken to be zero. At the boundary faces of the cube the potential rises to an indefinitely large value, so that the wave function of the particle vanishes at and outside these boundaries: this corresponds to the fact of the particle's imprisonment.

The standing wave pattern formed inside the box is then such that a whole number of half wavelengths occupies the distance a between each pair of opposite faces. This number need not be the same in the three different directions. Taking axes of x, y, z along the cube edges we have then wavelengths

$$\lambda_x = 2a/n_x$$

and corresponding momenta

$$p_x = n_x h/2a$$

so that the squared total momentum has value

$$p^2 = \frac{h^2}{4a^2}(n_x^2 + n_y^2 + n_z^2)$$

The distinct states can thus be represented as points in the space whose co-ordinates are p_x, p_y and p_z, with positions given by positive integer multiples of $h/2a$. Thus the volume of momentum space 'effectively occupied' by each state is $(h/2a)^3$, and in terms of the volume of configuration space $V (=a^3)$ available to the particle this is $h^3/8V$. In other words, the density of states in momentum space is $8V/h^3$, and, since only one octant of this space is being used, the number of states in the shell between p and $p+dp$ is on the average

$$\frac{8V}{h^3} \cdot \frac{\pi}{2} p^2 \, dp = \frac{4\pi V}{h^3} p^2 \, dp$$

It can be shown (with some difficulty) that this result holds for volumes of other shapes, the first correction term corresponding to a surface energy.

The kinetic energy of the particle is just $p^2/2m$, so the ground state has energy

$$\frac{3h^2}{8ma^2}$$

and the three next states have energy

$$\frac{3h^2}{4ma^2}$$

If then V or T is so large that

$$h^2/(mV^{2/3}) \ll kT$$

as will generally be the case when this model is of some actual use, the sum

$$Z = \sum_{n_x, n_y, n_z} \exp\left[-\frac{h^2}{8ma^2kT}(n_x^2+n_y^2+n_z^2)\right]$$

can be replaced by the integral

$$Z = \int_0^\infty \frac{4\pi V}{h^3} e^{-p^2/2mkT} p^2 \, dp$$

which is brought by a change of variable to standard form

$$Z = \frac{4\pi V}{h^3} (2mkT)^{3/2} \int_0^\infty x^2 e^{-x^2} \, dx$$

$$= \left(\frac{2\pi mkT}{h^2}\right)^{3/2} V$$

and hence (Reader: check this!)

$$U = \tfrac{3}{2}kT$$

$$S = k \ln V + \tfrac{3}{2}k \ln T + k \ln \left(\frac{2\pi mk}{h^2}\right)^{3/2} + \tfrac{3}{2}k$$

We have worked out this bit of wave mechanics in detail because of the great importance of the 'particle in a box' as an element in constructing models of more complicated systems. Obviously its most direct application will be to the thermodynamics of the ideal gas, but before discussing that we must look at a problem whose solution is at once constructed from results we have already obtained.

One heteronuclear diatomic molecule in a box

Evidently the configuration of the molecule is completely determined if we know the position of its centre of mass, the direction of its axis, and the separation of the atomic nuclei, provided that the electron system which holds it together remains in its ground state. If this is so we can ignore the detailed variation of the electron charge distribution during the movement of the molecule, and regard it simply as a background giving rise to an empirical force between the nuclei. This neglect is justified for most molecules at moderate temperatures.

The motion of the mass centre is independent of the other motions of the molecule; rotation and expansion are not quite independent, as is easily seen since angular momentum is conserved in the free motion of the molecule, so that angular speed must drop if moment of inertia increases. Moment of inertia is proportional to the square of the internuclear distance, so expansion or contraction of the molecule at constant angular momentum results in a changed angular speed and energy of rotation. Thus energy is exchanged between the rotary and vibratory motion of the molecule.

However, if the chemical binding force due to the electrons varies sharply enough with distance, the vibration of the nuclei along the axis of the molecule has high frequency and small amplitude, and the rotation and vibration can be treated as independent without serious error. Indeed, if the temperature is high enough for this to be unjustified, there is a substantial chance of the molecule being torn apart by the centrifugal force of its own rotation, and it becomes necessary to treat the dissociation equilibrium, which we shall come to later.

For moderate temperatures, then, we construct the partition function as a sum over states of energy ϵ, where distinct states are denoted by quantum numbers $\mathbf{n}_{tr}$, j, v referring to the translation, rotation and vibration of the molecule, and we have

$$\epsilon = \epsilon_{tr}(\mathbf{n}) + \epsilon_r(j) + \epsilon_v(v)$$
$$= \frac{p^2}{2m} + \frac{\hbar^2}{2A} j(j+1) + (v + \tfrac{1}{2})h\nu$$

where m is the total mass and A the moment of inertia of the molecule. The constituent parts of ϵ are sufficiently distinguished without the subscripts, so we drop those and write

$$
\begin{aligned}
Z &= \sum e^{-\epsilon/kT} \\
&= \sum e^{-(1/kT)[\epsilon(\mathbf{n}) + \epsilon(j) + \epsilon(v)]} \\
&= \left(\sum_{\mathbf{n}} e^{-\epsilon(\mathbf{n})/kT}\right) \cdot \left(\sum_j e^{-\epsilon(j)/kT}\right) \cdot \left(\sum_v e^{-\epsilon(v)/kT}\right) \\
&= Z_{tr} Z_j Z_v
\end{aligned}
$$

where Z_{tr}, Z_j, Z_v are the partition functions we have already calculated for the particle in a box, the rotor, and the harmonic oscillator.

Note that a factorization of the partition function in this way will always be possible when the energy of the system is a sum of quite independent terms. This is of course formally exactly the same position as we met in making the conceptual union of two physically distinct systems. Conversely, in the approximation we are using, the translation, rotation and vibration of the same molecule may be regarded as distinct physical systems, which might even be at different temperatures.

Such physical situations actually arise. Suppose for example that a gas which is in full thermal equilibrium is rapidly compressed. The translation of the molecules has no direct coupling to the rotation and vibration, so the increased kinetic energy of translation which arises from the adiabatic compression may leak relatively slowly, by molecular collisions, into these other modes of motion. The transfer of heat dQ from a system at T_1 to one at a lower temperature T_2 involves an increase of entropy $dQ(T_2^{-1} - T_1^{-1})$, so this dissipative process contributes to the damping of sound waves in gases with polyatomic molecules.

There is, as we have already seen, an intrinsic coupling between rotation and vibration. This is so contrained by conservation of angular momentum that the leakage of energy from rotation to vibration is also controlled by inter-molecular collisions.

The practical importance of the simple result obtained in this section is that the moment of inertia (or moments, for a non-linear molecule) and the frequencies of internal vibration of a molecule can be obtained by spectroscopic observation of the vapour. Such observations may be easier and are often much more precise than direct measurements of thermal properties over a wide temperature range, so that thermodynamic tables computed, using statistical mechanics, from spectroscopic data are often employed instead of direct observation. The detailed calculation is often rather more complicated, but the ideas are those that we have just discussed.

Negative absolute temperatures

At this stage we can deal with a topic which was hinted at in one of the problems of the introduction; namely, the existence of situations which are described by a negative absolute temperature. In such a situation the population of some group of energy states must increase with increasing energy according to the expression $\exp\left(-\epsilon/kT\right)$ which is now $\exp\left(\epsilon/k\,|T|\right)$. For this to make sense, the group of states must have an upper bound in energy.

Such an upper bound is not known to exist for any complete physical system, but it may well exist for the energy associated with a particular set of degrees of freedom. For example, in a non-paramagnetic substance containing hydrogen, the spins of the hydrogen protons are very weakly coupled to the other modes of motion of the system, particularly in the cold solid state. The spin motions then constitute a sub-system, and since the proton spin angular momentum is $\hbar/2$, the spin system is equivalent to a set of just such Fermi oscillators as were discussed above.

If for simplicity we neglect the magnetic action of the spinning protons on each other, only one typical proton need be considered, and the argument given before will apply. In the condition with the highest possible internal energy, the upper level is occupied with probability 1, and the lower with probability 0. This corresponds to the limit $T = -\delta$ as δ tends to zero. Both levels are equally occupied at both $T = +\infty$ and $T = -\infty$. The scale of rising energy runs from $T = +0$ to $T = +\infty$, which is the same as $T = -\infty$, and goes on rising from $T = -\infty$ to $T = -0$. Over the same range, the function $-T^{-1}$ runs continuously from $-\infty$ through 0 to $+\infty$. Note that all negative temperatures are hotter than all positive temperatures.

At a finite negative temperature the equilibrium magnetization per proton in a field H is again

$$m = -\mu \tanh\left(\mu H/kT\right)$$
$$= -\mu \tanh\left(\mu H/k\,|T|\right)$$

i.e. is opposed to H. It is true in general that when H is applied to a negative temperature magnetic system, instead of the field doing work on the system, energy is fed into the field. This will give rise to an actual power amplification in a suitable (i.e. resonant, in the sense that $h \times \text{frequency} = 2\mu H$) alternating field.

This unlikely sounding effect does occur and is the basis of masers and lasers. The practical problem is to find a moderately efficient way of producing the negative temperature state. This can be done for the protons by using a suitable pulse of coherent resonance radiation, which exactly inverts a spin distribution, equilibrated at ordinary temperature T, to give the distribution characteristic of $-T$. In other systems, e.g. the ruby laser, an intense flash of incoherent radiation (itself essentially at $T = \infty$) may suffice, through the population of high metastable levels surviving the pulse, while intermediate unstable levels depopulate rapidly towards the ground state.

In this last case, the notion of negative temperature can be applied only to the population ratio of a given pair of levels, and the whole distribution is not described by a temperature at all. Again, in an electric discharge, the electrons may be described by an electron temperature around $+10^4$ K, the gas atoms by a temperature around $+10^3$ K, and some particular pair of atomic or molecular excitations by a 'temperature' of -10^2 K.

Negative temperatures are easily understood and treated in the context of statistical mechanics. It is interesting to note that if the lowest and highest energy states of a system are both non-degenerate the entropy vanishes on both sides of absolute zero, that is, for the coldest and hottest conceivable states of the system. In general, the entropy need not be the same at $+0$ and -0 absolute.

Since, as noted above, all negative temperatures are hotter than all positive temperatures, special care must now be taken with the wording of the second law of thermodynamics. The standard form which survives is that due to Clausius—that heat cannot be transferred by a cyclic process from a cooler to a hotter body without other changes being simultaneously produced. The Kelvin form—that an amount of heat cannot be converted completely into work by a cyclic process without other changes being simultaneously produced—fails because a reservoir at negative temperature rises in entropy as it gives up energy, dropping towards negative infinite temperature. The principle must be qualified by saying 'heat from a reservoir at positive temperature' and an inverse impossibility stated, that of converting an amount of work into heat supplied to an object at negative temperature by a cyclic process with no other effects.

The ideal insulating crystal

In a crystal which is a good insulator the whole electron structure remains in its ground state practically all the time, except while at very high temperature, since the least energy required to excite an electron is several electron volts. Thus, to understand the thermo-dynamic behaviour at moderate temperatures we need only consider the movements of the atomic nuclei in the crystal. These can be considered as point particles for the present purpose.

Since the crystal as a whole obeys Hooke's law for small strains, the restoring force on an atom must be a linear function of its displacement with respect to its neighbours, so long as this displacement is a small fraction of the interatomic distance. Thus for a crystal containing N atoms we shall obtain $3N$ linear equations of motion in the absence of external forces.

These $3N$ equations can be imagined combined to give three equations expressing the constancy of linear momentum of the whole system, three equations expressing the constancy of angular momentum of the whole system and $3N-6$ equations of harmonic oscillation describing the oscillatory normal modes of the crystal. Alternatively, we may change the physical picture by supposing the crystal constrained, for example, by spring plates pressing against its faces. The motions of translation and rotation of the whole crystal will then be oscillatory, and the equations of motion of the surface atoms will have additional terms added in, corresponding to the pressure of the plates against them. However, for a crystal containing many milliards of atoms, these changes produce very little change in the distribution of the normal oscillations, most of which will be shifted in frequency by a fraction of the order of the reciprocal of the number of atoms in a diameter of the crystal. The total effect of this will be the appearance of extra terms, proportional to surface area, in the thermodynamic functions. These we ignore for the present.

Since there are very many modes of lattice vibration, we summarize them by a distribution $g(v)$ which is defined by the statement that the number of modes whose frequencies lie in the interval from v to $v+dv$ is $g(v)\,dv$. We must then have

$$\int_0^\infty g(v)\,dv = 3N$$

and for all but the smallest crystals $g(v)$ depends on N only by a multiplying factor, so that $g'(v)/g(v)$ is independent of N.

The density function $g(v)$ can be determined by arbitrary fiat, plausible argument, or appeal to experiment, the choice depending on the intended use of the results. The simplest assumption, due to Einstein, is that we are to consider each atom oscillating as if its neighbours are at rest in their equilibrium positions. Provided all atomic positions are equivalent, this gives at most three distinct frequencies, and every atom has a motion compounded of these frequencies, so that in particular

$$\frac{U}{N} = \frac{h}{2} (\nu_1 + \nu_2 + \nu_3) + \sum_{i=1,2,3} \frac{h\nu_i}{e^{h\nu_i/kT} - 1}$$

At high temperatures $U \sim 3NkT$, which corresponds to Dulong and Petit's law. Moreover, the specific heat falls off for $kT \lesssim h\nu_{min}$, which corresponds to the drop in the measured specific heat of crystals at low temperature. Unfortunately the specific heat of this model goes to zero, at very low temperatures, as

$$T^{-2} e^{-h\nu_{min}/kT}$$

which is very much faster than the observed rate.

A more plausible model is due to Debye, who pointed out that, whatever the complete lattice spectrum may look like, the low frequency modes must correspond to the normal modes of oscillation of a block of elastic continuum of the same size, and with the same elastic constants as the crystal. Since, at low enough temperature, all the high frequency oscillations are frozen out, in their ground state, and are not contributing to the specific heat, this model should give the low temperature specific heat correctly. It is obviously correct at high temperatures, as is the Einstein model.

Consider a cube of edge a composed of an isotropic elastic substance. The vibrations of such a material can be resolved into longitudinal waves, in which the elastic displacement is normal to the wave front, and transverse waves, in which the displacement lies within the wave front. For a given wavelength and direction of propagation, there may occur one longitudinal wave, and two independent transverse waves in which the displacement directions are mutually perpendicular.

To define the problem, suppose that the faces of the cube are pressed against planes of some extremely hard substance, so that displacements there are zero. Then the modes of oscillation of the cube will have exactly the same pattern as the de Broglie waves we discussed before for a particle moving in a cubical box, and corresponding to the mode numbers n_x, n_y, n_z we have a wavelength λ such that

$$k^2 \equiv \lambda^{-2} = \frac{1}{4a^2} (n_x^2 + n_y^2 + n_z^2)$$

The volume of k-space 'occupied' by each mode is $(2a)^{-3}$ or $1/8V$.

The number of modes occurring on the average between k and $k + dk$ is therefore

$$4\pi V k^2 \, dk$$

Corresponding to each mode are three distinct wave motions, propagating with two speeds, c_l for the longitudinal wave and c_t for the transverse waves. For large wavelength and low frequency these speeds are constant and equal to the speeds of sound. At high frequencies, c will depend on k in some way not very easy to predict.

The thermal behaviour of the oscillations depends on their frequency, which is related to the wavenumber by

$$\nu = kc$$

so that the number of oscillations between frequencies ν and $\nu + d\nu$ is

$$4\pi V(c_l^{-3} + 2c_t^{-3})\nu^2 \, d\nu = 12\pi V c^{-3} \nu^2 \, d\nu$$

where c is the average speed defined by

$$3c^{-3} = c_l^{-3} + 2c_t^{-3}$$

This value for the number of distinct oscillations will be correct at fairly low frequencies. The limit of $3N$ on the total number of oscillations implies that there will be a maximum k, k_m, such that

$$4\pi V \int_0^{k_m} k^2 \, dk = N$$

i.e.
$$\frac{4\pi}{3} k_m^3 = \frac{N}{V}$$

the number density of atoms in the material. Thus k_m is of the order of the reciprocal of the nearest-neighbour distance between atoms. This k_m will be the same for longitudinal and transverse waves, so maximum frequencies will not be the same, and there will be a band of frequencies in which only one type of oscillation occurs.

However, deeper examination shows that dispersion, i.e. the varying speed of the waves, causes worse complications than this at high frequency. Thus we do the model no real injustice by the apparently inconsistent procedure of assuming a density of oscillations in frequency simply proportional to ν^2, up to a ν_m defined by

$$12\pi V c^{-3} \int_0^{\nu_m} \nu^2 \, d\nu = 3N$$

i.e.

$$\nu_m = ck_m$$

$$= c\left(\frac{3N}{4\pi V}\right)^{1/3}$$

This maximum frequency ν_m is characteristic of the material, not of the sample, and is used to define the Debye temperature θ_D by the relation

$$h\nu_m = k\theta_D$$

The Debye temperature can be predicted from the speed of sound in the material and its number density, but is often treated as an empirical parameter to be fitted to the low temperature specific heat data. (The true $g(\nu)$ can be found from X-ray and neutron scattering experiments.)

The number of oscillations between frequencies ν and $\nu + d\nu$ can now be written as

$$9N\frac{\nu^2\,d\nu}{\nu_m^3}$$

and the internal energy per atom is, omitting the zero-point energy,

$$\frac{U}{N} = \frac{9}{\nu_m^3}\int_0^{\nu_m}\frac{h\nu}{e^{h\nu/kT}-1}\,\nu^2\,d\nu$$

$$= \frac{9k}{\theta_D^3}\int_0^{\theta_D}\frac{\theta^3\,d\theta}{e^{\theta/T}-1}$$

The integral is a tabulated function of T/θ_D. For very low T,

$$\frac{U}{N} \sim \frac{9k}{\theta_D^3}\int_0^{\infty}\theta^3\,e^{-\theta/T}\,d\theta$$

where the very rapid decrease of the exponential allows us to replace θ_D by infinity at the upper limit of integration.

Thus

$$\frac{U}{N} \sim \frac{54kT^4}{\theta_D^3}$$

and the specific heat per atom

$$C_V \sim \frac{216kT^3}{\theta_D^3}$$

That $C_V \propto T^3$ for small T is in good agreement with experiment, and to this extent the Debye model is entirely successful. It is less successful at intermediate temperatures where the less regularly distributed high frequency oscillations are coming into play.

Black body radiation

Closely related to the problem of elastic waves treated in the previous section is the case of electromagnetic radiation in thermal equilibrium. We consider a cavity of volume V whose walls are at temperature T. If the walls are almost perfect reflectors, the tangential electric field must vanish at the walls, and the permitted wave patterns are the same as for the particle in a box. The only change is that the patterns with one of n_x, n_y or $n_z = 0$ are now possible, which was not the case before; these however contribute only to the surface-dependent part of the energy, and not to the bulk energy. For the wave patterns with n_x, n_y and n_z non-zero there are two independent states of polarization possible, so the number of independent oscillations with wave numbers in the range k to $k + dk$ is

$$8\pi V k^2 \, dk$$

Of course, if the walls are quite perfect reflectors there is no mechanism for the emission or absorption of radiation, but we are concerned only with the thermal equilibrium state, and the least imperfection in the reflection of any part of the wall will enable this equilibrium to be reached eventually, without perceptibly disturbing the spectrum of the cavity oscillations.

The speed of light in vacuum c, is the same for all k, so the frequency of an oscillation of wavenumber k is ck and the quantum of energy associated with it is $hck = h\nu$. The number of oscillations in the range of frequencies from ν to $\nu + d\nu$ is

$$\frac{8\pi V}{c^3} \nu^2 \, d\nu$$

so the density of energy in the field is

$$\frac{U}{V} = \frac{8\pi}{c^3} \int_0^\infty \frac{h\nu}{e^{h\nu/kT} - 1} \nu^2 \, d\nu$$

where the upper limit of frequency is infinite since, so far as we know, there is no natural upper bound to the frequency of possible photons. Then, with a change of variable,

$$\frac{U}{V} = 8\pi hc \left(\frac{kT}{hc}\right)^4 \int_0^\infty \frac{x^3 \, dx}{e^x - 1}$$

Now

$$\int_0^\infty \frac{x^3 \, \mathrm{d}x}{\mathrm{e}^x - 1} = \int_0^\infty \frac{x^3 \, \mathrm{e}^{-x} \mathrm{d}x}{1 - \mathrm{e}^{-x}}$$

and since $\exp(-x) < 1$ for $x > 0$ we can write

$$\int_0^\infty \frac{x^3 \, \mathrm{e}^{-x}}{1 - \mathrm{e}^{-x}} \, \mathrm{d}x = \int_0^\infty x^3 \, \mathrm{e}^{-x}(1 + \mathrm{e}^{-x} + \mathrm{e}^{-2x} + \cdots) \, \mathrm{d}x$$

$$= \sum_{n=1}^\infty \int_0^\infty x^3 \, \mathrm{e}^{-nx} \, \mathrm{d}x$$

$$= \sum_{n=1}^\infty n^{-4} \int_0^\infty x^3 \, \mathrm{e}^{-x} \, \mathrm{d}x$$

$$= 6 \sum_{n=1}^\infty n^{-4}$$

The series $\sum n^{-4}$ converges rapidly. This sum is called $\zeta(4)$ where $\xi(s) \equiv \sum n^{-s}$ for real or complex s is known as Riemann's ζ-function. The evaluation of the ζ-function is not elementary, so we just take the value $\pi^4/90$ from tables, and end with the energy density

$$\frac{U}{V} = \frac{8\pi hc}{15} \left(\frac{\pi kT}{hc}\right)^4$$

$$= \frac{8\pi^2}{15} \, kT \left(\frac{\pi kT}{hc}\right)^3$$

We see, first, that U/V is proportional to T^4, in agreement with Stefan's law, and secondly, that if we define a certain wavelength λ_0 of the thermal radiation by $\lambda_0 = hc/(\pi kT)$, we have

$$\frac{U}{V} = \frac{8\pi^2}{15} \cdot \frac{kT}{\lambda_0^3}$$

$$\sim 6 \frac{kT}{\lambda_0^3}$$

which can be expressed verbally by saying that energy kT is associated with each direction of polarization (2) and propagation (3) in each volume λ_0^3, where the characteristic distance λ_0 is itself inversely proportional to kT. The differential energy density associated with the frequency interval $\mathrm{d}\nu$ at ν which is

$$\frac{\mathrm{d}U}{V} = \frac{8\pi h}{c^3} \frac{\nu^3 \, \mathrm{d}\nu}{\mathrm{e}^{h\nu/kT} - 1}$$

can be expressed in terms of the corresponding wavelength $\lambda = c/\nu$ as

$$\frac{8\pi hc}{\lambda^5} \frac{\mathrm{d}\lambda}{e^{\pi\lambda_0/\lambda} - 1}$$

If $\lambda \ll \lambda_0$, this expression is dominated by the exponential term and becomes

$$\frac{\mathrm{d}U}{V} = \frac{8\pi hc}{\lambda^5} e^{-\pi\lambda_0/\lambda} \, \mathrm{d}\lambda$$

while if $\lambda \gg \lambda_0$, in the far infra-red, we can expand the exponential and obtain

$$\frac{\mathrm{d}U}{V} = \frac{8\pi kT}{\lambda^4} \, \mathrm{d}\lambda$$

3

SYSTEMS OF IDENTICAL PARTICLES

Physical identity

The simple systems of the previous chapter had the common feature that they contained only a single motion or an easily identified set of completely independent motions, so that the distinct quantum states of each system were enumerated in a perfectly straightforward way. The reader's attention has already been drawn, in the section on the rotor, to the next problem that must be faced: systems composed of identical particles have certain restrictions on the states of motion which are accessible to them.

These restrictions are most easily understood in terms of the wave function which describes a pure state of such a system. This is a complex function $\mathcal{F}(\mathbf{r}, \ldots, \mathbf{r}', \ldots)$ of the positions and spins of all the particles of the system, such that $\mathcal{F}^*\mathcal{F}\,d\mathbf{r}\ldots d\mathbf{r}'\ldots$ measures the probability that the system in the given pure state should be found in the range of configurations $\mathbf{r} \rightarrow \mathbf{r} + d\mathbf{r}, \ldots, \mathbf{r}' \rightarrow \mathbf{r}' + d\mathbf{r}', \ldots.$ $\mathcal{F}^*$ is complex conjugate to $\mathcal{F}$. Here $\mathbf{r}$ must be taken to include both position and spin co-ordinates. Now it appears that identical particles are in fact so strongly identical that the physical situation which arises when two of them are interchanged is exactly the same as the original. This can only be so if the corresponding wave function

$$\mathcal{F}(\mathbf{r}', \ldots, \mathbf{r}, \ldots)$$

differs from the original

$$\mathcal{F}(\mathbf{r}, \ldots, \mathbf{r}', \ldots)$$

only through multiplication by some (possibly complex) number of modulus 1. Since a repetition of the same exchange gives us back a situation which is formally as well as physically identical with the original, the square of this number is 1 and its only possible values are $+1$ and -1.

Moreover, if we have identical particles A, B, C in the same system, the exchange of A and B may be achieved directly or by the sequence, B with C, A with C, and B with C again. Thus the effect of the exchange of A with B on the wave function must involve the same multiplying factor as the exchange of A with C, and the same again (using AC, BC, AC) as the exchange of B with C. Thus in a given system the exchange of any pair of identical particles of a given species multiplies the wave function by the same number $+1$ or -1. The sign might still vary from system to system as well as from species to species.

It turns out that all the elementary particles fall into two classes known respectively as bosons and fermions. Bosons have a spin angular momentum of zero or an integral multiple of $\hbar$; fermions have a spin which is half of an odd integral multiple of $\hbar$ (all the fundamental fermions known at present have spin $\hbar/2$). Electrons, nucleons and compound objects containing odd numbers of these particles (e.g. H or He^3 atoms) are fermions; photons, π-mesons and compound objects containing even numbers of fermions (e.g. He^4 atoms) are bosons.

The wave function of a system is unaltered by the exchange of two bosons of the same sort; it changes sign on the exchange of two fermions of the same sort. Since the wave function, which is continuous, must then vanish whenever two like fermions have the same co-ordinates, it follows that two like fermions can never coincide in both position and spin.

Another expression of the rule for identical fermions is the familiar exclusion principle of Pauli: if the state of the whole system is constructed from a set of independent single-particle states, no two identical fermions can occupy the same state.

Ortho- and parahydrogen

In the H_2 molecule the two protons are fermions. The symmetry of the wave function with respect to exchange of the positions of the protons is determined by the rotational quantum number, j, the effect of the exchange being to multiply the wave function by $(-1)^j$. Since the effect of exchanging both position and spin must be to multiply the wave function by -1, the effect of exchanging spins alone is to multiply by -1 for even j and by $+1$ for odd j. The one antisymmetric spin wave function corresponds to antiparallel

spins, giving one state of zero total spin angular momentum: the
three symmetric spin wave functions correspond to parallel spins,
giving the three distinct states of orientation of a unit total spin
angular momentum.

Since there is no dynamical interaction compelling the exchange of
angular momentum between the proton spins and the rotation of the
whole molecule, the stationary states of the molecule fall into two
families: orthohydrogen with odd j and parallel proton spins: and
parahydrogen with even j and antiparallel proton spins. The ground
state, with $j = 0$, belongs to parahydrogen and lies distinctly below
the first ortho-state at $j = 1$, so that at very low temperature hydrogen
molecules should be practically all in the parahydrogen ground state.

In the absence of a strong magnetic field, which would orient the
magnetic moments of the protons, the different spin states make no
contribution to the energy, so the partition function for the rotation
of the molecule can in general be written

$$Z = Z_p + 3Z_0$$

where Z_p and Z_0 are sums over the states with even and odd j respectively. If $T \gg \theta$, the rotational characteristic temperature previously
defined, then

$$Z_p = Z_0 = T/(2\theta)$$

and the ratio of parahydrogen to orthohydrogen in the equilibrium
mixture is just 1 to 3.

Two interesting points now arise. The first is that hydrogen molecules, even in the liquid, apparently rotate with very little mutual
interference, so that the distinction of ortho- and parahydrogen is
still valid even in the cold liquid. The second is that the very weak
coupling between the proton spins and the molecular rotation makes
the transformation of ortho- to parahydrogen exceedingly slow. In
fact, the transformation has to be catalysed by the very high varying
magnetic field of a paramagnetic atom or molecule (e.g. dissolved O_2
or a metal surface) to proceed at a useful rate. Hydrogen liquefied
without catalysed conversion will contain three parts of orthohydrogen to one of parahydrogen, and the approach to the equilibrium ratio is a thoroughly irreversible process, taking place at
paramagnetic centres in the container walls. The heat liberated in
this process is enough to cause an alarming evaporation loss on
storage.

Note that in the classical limit, $T \gg \theta$, $Z \sim 2T/\theta$, where one would
expect for distinguishable particles of spin $\frac{1}{2}$ to have $2 \times 2 \times T/\theta$—a

factor of 2 for each particle. In this limit, then, the identity of two particles just halves the 'classically' expected partition function.

The ideal gas—Gibbs' paradox

Our molecular model of an ideal gas will consist of N similar particles moving without interaction in a volume V. If their movements were totally independent and the particles were all distinct, we should then expect a partition function

$$Z_N = Z_1^N$$

where

$$Z_1 = \left(\frac{2\pi mkT}{h^2}\right)^{3/2} V$$

as we found before for a single particle. It is easy to show that this leads to results in contradiction with experience.

The entropy of a single molecule moving in V has been found to be

$$S_1(V) = k \ln V + \tfrac{3}{2}k \ln T + k \ln \left(\frac{2\pi mk}{h^2}\right)^{3/2} + \tfrac{3}{2}k$$

If $Z_N = Z_1^N$, we should then have

$$S_N(V) = R \ln V + \tfrac{3}{2}R \ln T + R \ln \left(\frac{2\pi mk}{h^2}\right)^{3/2} + \tfrac{3}{2}R$$

where $R = Nk$. Now suppose we have two volumes, each V, each containing N molecules and separated from each other by a valve. The total entropy is $2S_N(V)$. If the valve is now opened, the whole volume $2V$ is accessible to every molecule, and the entropy should be

$$S_{2N}(2V) = 2R \ln 2V + 3R \ln T + 2R \ln \left(\frac{2\pi mk}{h^2}\right)^{3/2} + 3R$$
$$= 2S_N(V) + 2R \ln 2$$

The entropy of mixing, $2R \ln 2$, does indeed appear when two *different* gases diffuse into each other, but does *not* appear when we have the identical gas in the two volumes. The difficulty is removed when we recognize the indistinguishability of physically identical molecules.

We consider first a system consisting of only two identical bodies.

Two non-interacting identical particles

The protons in the hydrogen molecule are almost rigidly connected together. We now consider two particles which have no dynamical interaction, their movement being controlled by an external field of force which is the same for both. The change in behaviour of each particle in the presence of the other is thus determined entirely by the indistinguishability of the particles and their character as bosons or fermions.

Let the distinct energy states of one particle in the external field have energy α_i. If $i \neq j$, there is *one* state of the system with energy $\epsilon = \alpha_i + \alpha_j$. If $i = j$, there is *one* state of the system with $\epsilon = 2\alpha_i$ provided the particles are bosons: there is no such state if the particles are fermions. Thus the partition function for this system is

$$Z = \tfrac{1}{2} \sum_{i \neq j} e^{-(\alpha_i + \alpha_j)/kT} \left(+ \sum_i e^{-2\alpha_i/kT} \text{ for bosons} \right)$$

where the factor $\tfrac{1}{2}$ in the first term is needed because each single-particle state occurs once in the sum over i and again in the sum over j, so that every pair i, j is named twice in the sum. This can be re-written as

$$Z = \tfrac{1}{2} \sum_{i,j} e^{-(\alpha_i + \alpha_j)/kT} \pm \tfrac{1}{2} \sum_i e^{-2\alpha_i/kT}$$

where the first sum is now without restriction on i and j; the upper sign is valid for bosons and the lower for fermions. This is the same as

$$Z = \tfrac{1}{2} Z_1^2 \pm \tfrac{1}{2} \sum e^{-2\alpha_i/kT}$$

We see that this differs from the expression $Z = Z_1^2$, which one expects for distinct particles, in two ways. First, the factor $\tfrac{1}{2}$ accounts for the identity of the particles: second, the situations where both particles are in the same state are emphasized for bosons and excluded for fermions.

The hot ideal gas—Gibbs' paradox resolved

If we have N identical particles and T is so high that $\alpha_N \ll kT$, the particles will wander over many times N one-particle states, so that the main part of the partition function is obtained by considering only those states of the system in which each particle is in a different one-particle state. Since there is only *one* state with one particle in α_i, one in α_j and so on, while the expression Z_1^N names each such state $N!$ times (in every possible order of the indices $i, j, \ldots$), this main part of the partition function is entirely included in

$$\frac{1}{N!} Z_1^N$$

This expression includes terms in which several particles are in the same one-particle state. These must be supplemented for bosons or excluded for fermions, so we have

$$Z = \frac{1}{N!} Z_1^N + \text{corrections for particle character}$$

At sufficiently high T the correction terms can be neglected, and we have

$$Z \sim \frac{1}{N!} \left(\frac{2\pi mkT}{h^2}\right)^{3N/2} V^N$$

Using only the leading terms $\ln N! \sim N \ln N - N$ in Stirling's approximation, we have now for the entropy

$$\begin{aligned}
S_N(V) &= R \ln V + \tfrac{3}{2} R \ln T + R \ln \left(\frac{2\pi mk}{h^2}\right)^{3/2} \\
&\quad + \tfrac{3}{2}R - R \ln N + R \\
&= R \ln \frac{V}{N} + \tfrac{3}{2} R \ln T + R \ln \left(\frac{2\pi mk}{h^2}\right)^{3/2} + \tfrac{5}{2}R,
\end{aligned}$$

where $R = Nk$—a very important result in agreement with the familiar thermodynamic behaviour of the entropy.

We must now find out at what temperatures the correction terms begin to matter, and calculate their form. This part of the work is enormously simplified if we discuss first of all a more general statistical question than was previously considered.

The grand partition function

Devices which measure quantities of gas very seldom determine mass, or number of molecules, directly. Usually one measures pressure and volume at known temperature, and deduces the mass using an equation of state. Even when a direct weighing is made, it is never so accurate that the number of molecules present is known to plus or minus one (or one million, if it comes to that). Thus no physical verisimilitude is really lost if we treat the number $\bar{N}$ of particles in our physical system as a statistical expectation value just as we did with U. We can of course choose to discuss systems in which the number N of particles present does obviously vary with time; for example, a small fixed volume in a region occupied by matter, where particles are continually wandering in and out.

We consider then a system which contains a variable number N of particles of the same sort. Let the distinct energy states of the system when it contains N particles be $\epsilon_i(N)$, and suppose that they have associated with them probabilities $p_i(N)$ such that

$$\sum_i \sum_N p_i(N) = 1$$

The information carried by this set of probabilities is

$$H = \sum_i \sum_N p_i(N) \ln [p_i(N)]$$

and we now enquire what choice of the $p_i(N)$ minimizes this H subject to the further conditions

$$\sum_i \sum_N N p_i(N) = \overline{N}$$

$$\sum_i \sum_N \epsilon_i(N) p_i(N) = U$$

where the expectation values $\overline{N}$ and U are given.

All we have to do is to introduce another Lagrange multiplier, and we find for the least informative set of p_i consistent with the given conditions

$$p_i(N) = \Xi^{-1} e^{\nu N - \beta \epsilon_i(N)}$$

where

$$\Xi = \sum_{i,N} e^{\nu N - \beta \epsilon_i(N)}$$

is called the grand partition function. We note that

$$\Xi = \sum e^{\nu N} Z(N)$$

where $Z(N)$ is our previous partition function for the system with exactly N particles. If we define Ω to be $\ln \Xi$, then

$$\overline{N} = \frac{\partial \ln \Xi}{\partial \nu} = \frac{\partial \Omega}{\partial \nu}$$

and

$$U = -\frac{\partial \Omega}{\partial \beta}$$

To re-establish connection with thermodynamics, we have to recall a little more of the thermodynamics than we have used hitherto. A useful thermodynamic function closely related to the Helmholtz free energy $F (= U - TS)$ is the Gibbs free energy

$$G = U + PV - TS$$

where P, V represent pressure and volume, and U, T, S are internal energy, temperature and entropy as before. The chemical potential μ_c of any component is defined by $\mu_c = \partial G/\partial \bar{N}_c$, where $\bar{N}_c$ is the number of molecules of that component present in the system. If the system is made to grow at constant temperature and pressure by feeding in new material in such proportions that the concentrations of the various components remain constant, the μ_c remain constant as total mass and volume increase, so we see that G can be expressed as a sum over the components

$$G = \sum_c \bar{N}_c \mu_c$$

and for a one component system

$$G = \bar{N}\mu$$

If two systems 1, 2 are brought into contact so that they can exchange both material and energy, the conditions of thermodynamic equilibrium between them are that, for all components,

$$\mu_{c,1} = \mu_{c,2}$$

and that

$$T_1 = T_2$$

If, in addition, there is no mechanical barrier between them (such as a stiff, permeable membrane) there is a condition of mechanical equilibrium $P_1 = P_2$, but such barriers occur in many interesting situations, for example, as biological cell membranes.

Reverting to the statistical picture, consider two systems characterized by $\bar{N}_1$, U_1 and $\bar{N}_2$, U_2, and the corresponding ν_1, β_1 and ν_2, β_2. If we make a conceptual union of the two systems, the situation

$$N_1, \; \epsilon_i(N_1), \; N_2, \; \epsilon_j(N_2)$$

will occur with probability

$$p[N_1, \epsilon_i(N_1); N_2, \epsilon_j(N_2)] = \exp\left[\nu_1 N_1 + \nu_2 N_2 - \beta_1 \epsilon_i(N_1) - \beta_2 \epsilon_j(N_2)\right]$$

This probability is unaltered, on changing the conceptual union to a physical one in which matter and energy are freely exchanged between the two systems, only if it is equivalent to

$$\exp\left\{\nu(N_1 + N_2) - \beta[\epsilon_i(N_1) + \epsilon_j(N_2)]\right\}$$

for all N, ϵ. This can only be true if $\nu_1 = \nu_2 = \nu$, $\beta_1 = \beta_2 = \beta$. Thus the statistical conditions $\nu_1 = \nu_2$, $\beta_1 = \beta_2$ are together equivalent to the thermodynamic conditions $\mu_1 = \mu_2$, $T_1 = T_2$.

To identify ν and β more closely we consider how Ω ($= \ln \Xi$)

depends on ν, β and the ϵ. The change in Ω produced by small changes in these variables is

$$d\Omega = \frac{\partial\Omega}{\partial\nu}\,d\nu + \frac{\partial\Omega}{\partial\beta}\,d\beta + \sum_{i,N}\frac{\partial\Omega}{\partial\epsilon_i(N)}\,d\epsilon_i(N)$$

$$= \bar{N}\,d\nu - U\,d\beta - \beta\sum_{i,N}p_i(N)\,d\epsilon_i(N)$$

The form of this suggests that we look at the variation of $\Omega + U\beta - \bar{N}\nu$, which is then, from the above equation

$$d(\Omega + U\beta - \bar{N}\nu) = -\nu\,d\bar{N} + \beta\,dQ$$

where dQ is $\sum_{i,N}\epsilon_i(N)\,dp_i(N)$ as before. In particular, for a fixed value of $\bar{N}$ we have

$$d(\Omega + U\beta - \bar{N}\nu) = \beta\,dQ$$

so β is an integrating factor for the heat increment dQ. Since the function $\Omega + U\beta - \bar{N}\nu$ is additive when independent systems are united (conceptually, or, if they are in thermodynamic equilibrium, by physical contact), β is $1/kT$ as before. We then have

$$d(\Omega + U/(kT) - \bar{N}\nu) = dS/k$$

and since we already have

$$PV + U - \bar{N}\mu = TS$$

we have

$$\frac{1}{kT}(PV - \bar{N}\mu) = \Omega - \bar{N}\nu$$

or

$$\frac{1}{kT}\left(\frac{P}{\rho} - \mu\right) = \frac{\Omega}{\bar{N}} - \nu$$

Now, μ/kT and ν differ only by a function of temperature. Since PV and $\bar{N}$ are independently variable at given T, for all systems other than a Boyle gas, the terms in the last equation are set independently equal, so that

$$\nu = \frac{\mu}{kT}$$

and

$$\Omega = \frac{PV}{kT}$$

We have, finally, an alternative statistical expression of thermodynamics in terms of the grand partition function Ξ, for which

$$e^{PV/kT} = \Xi = \sum_{N,i}e^{(1/kT)[\mu N - \epsilon_i(N)]}$$

where μ is the chemical potential, so that the mean number of particles present is

$$\bar{N} = kT \frac{\partial \ln \Xi}{\partial \mu}$$

and the internal energy

$$U = -\frac{\partial \ln \Xi}{\partial \beta}$$

Non-interacting identical particles

Since the statistical character of fermions and bosons only affects the behaviour of gases composed of them at temperatures and concentrations where the forces of interaction between the particles are also important, it is unprofitable to consider gases of polyatomic molecules in this chapter. We shall consider only gases of one component, made up of atoms or of sub-atomic particles.

Suppose that we have non-interacting particles at chemical potential μ and temperature T, moving in a containing field in which the energy levels of individual particles are α_i. Since the particles are indistinguishable, a steady configuration of the system is completely determined by the set of numbers n_i of particles in the set of levels α_i. This whole set is conveniently denoted by **n**. The energy of the system in this configuration is then

$$\epsilon_{\mathbf{n}} = \sum_i n_i \alpha_i$$

and the total number of particles present is

$$N = \sum_i n_i$$

The grand partition function of this system is thus

$$\Xi = \sum_{\mathbf{n}} \exp\left[\frac{1}{kT}(\mu N - \epsilon)\right]$$

$$= \sum_{\mathbf{n}} \exp\left[\frac{1}{kT}\left(\mu \sum n_i - \sum n_i \alpha_i\right)\right]$$

$$= \sum_{\mathbf{n}} \prod_i e^{(n_i/kT)(\mu - \alpha_i)}$$

$$= \sum_{\mathbf{n}} \prod_i t_i^{n_i} = \prod_i \left(\sum_{n_i} t_i^{n_i}\right)$$

where $t_i = \exp[(\mu - \alpha_i)/kT]$. The **n** over which the sum is taken include only those partitions of the N which are permitted by the statistical character of the particles. For bosons, all partitions are admissible, while for fermions the n_i can only be one or zero. It is then easy to see that for bosons

$$\Xi = \prod_i (1 + t_i + t_i^2 + \cdots)$$

$$= \prod_i \frac{1}{1 - t_i}$$

while for fermions

$$\Xi = \prod_i (1 + t_i)$$

Briefly,

$$\Xi = \prod_i (1 \mp t_i)^{\mp 1}$$

where each upper sign is valid for bosons, and the lower for fermions. This convention will be used hereafter.

An important probability in this situation is the probability $p_i(n_i)$ of finding exactly n_i particles in level α_i, irrespective of what is happening elsewhere. This is evidently Ξ^{-1} times the sum of all the terms in Ξ for which the exponent of t_i is n_i, and we see by inspecting the structure of Ξ that

$$p_i(n_i) = t_i^{n_i}(1 \mp t_i)^{\pm 1}$$

The expectation value $\langle n_i \rangle$ of n_i is then at once, for fermions,

$$\langle n_i \rangle = \frac{0 + t_i}{1 + t_i} = (t_i^{-1} + 1)^{-1}$$

Using the identity $\sum_{n=1}^{\infty} n t^n = t/(1-t)^2$, we find for bosons,

$$\langle n_i \rangle = \frac{t_i}{(1 - t_i)^2} (1 - t_i) = (t_i^{-1} - 1)^{-1}$$

so that in general

$$\langle n_i \rangle = \frac{1}{e^{(\alpha_i - \mu)/kT} \mp 1}$$

These distributions are the well-known distribution laws due to Bose and Einstein and to Fermi and Dirac respectively. The derivation presented here has the surprising merit of being both honest and easy.

The next step is to specify some potential energy which defines the α_i, and calculate the consequences.

The ideal monatomic gas at chemical potential μ

As before, we consider a volume V within which the gas atoms move at zero potential energy, the potential energy increasing sharply to an effectively infinite value at the boundary. If the magnitude of momentum of a gas atom of mass m is p, its kinetic energy is $p^2/2m$; the substitution $x = p/\sqrt{2mkT}$, $\zeta = e^{\mu/kT}$ then gives (see p. 30)

$$\bar{N} = 4\pi V \left(\frac{2mkT}{h^2}\right)^{3/2} \int_0^\infty \frac{x^2 \, \mathrm{d}x}{\zeta^{-1} e^{x^2} \mp 1}$$

$$U = 4\pi VkT \left(\frac{2mkT}{h^2}\right)^{3/2} \int_0^\infty \frac{x^4 \, \mathrm{d}x}{\zeta^{-1} e^{x^2} \mp 1}$$

$$F = \bar{N}\mu - kT \ln \Xi$$

$$= \bar{N}\mu \pm 4\pi VkT \left(\frac{2mkT}{h^2}\right)^{3/2} \int_0^\infty \ln\left(1 \mp \zeta e^{-x^2}\right) x^2 \, \mathrm{d}x$$

Evidently the parameter ζ is non-negative: we see further that for bosons, if $\zeta > 1$, the integrals have an unmanageable singularity at $x = \sqrt{\mu/kT}$, so that for bosons μ is necessarily negative; μ may be assigned any positive or negative value for fermions without trouble arising.

Hot dilute ideal gas

The expression for $\bar{N}$ given above serves to determine ζ if the numerical density $n \equiv \bar{N}/V$ and the temperature T are given. Evidently ζ is less for larger T and lower n. If ζ is small enough, the positive or negative unit in the denominator of the integrand is negligible compared with ζ^{-1} and we may write

$$n = 4\pi\zeta \left(\frac{2mkT}{h^2}\right)^{3/2} \int_0^\infty x^2 e^{-x^2} \, \mathrm{d}x$$

$$= \zeta \left(\frac{2\pi mkT}{h^2}\right)^{3/2}$$

so $\zeta = n\Lambda^3$, where $\Lambda = h/\sqrt{2\pi mkT}$ is the characteristic wavelength of the particle at T, i.e. ζ is the number of particles in the characteristic volume.

Correspondingly, $U = \frac{3}{2}\bar{N}kT$, reproducing our previous result for the hot dilute gas with fixed composition $N = \bar{N}$.

Cold dense ideal gas

For larger values of ζ, bosons and fermions behave very differently indeed, and require separate discussion. Their divergences from high-temperature behaviour are called by the oddly chosen name of degeneration.

Bose–Einstein degeneration

We have seen that ζ for a gas of bosons cannot be more than one; we consider first the limiting situation where $\zeta = 1$. Then the numerical density is given by

$$n_l = 4\pi \left(\frac{2mkT}{h^2}\right)^{3/2} \int_0^\infty \frac{x^2 \, dx}{e^{x^2} - 1}$$

The integral is quite tractable by the device used in the section on black body radiation.

$$\int_0^\infty \frac{x^2 \, dx}{e^{x^2} - 1} = \int_0^\infty \frac{x^2 \, e^{-x^2} \, dx}{1 - e^{-x^2}}$$

$$= \sum_{n=1}^\infty \int_0^\infty x^2 \, e^{-nx^2} \, dx$$

$$= \sum n^{-3/2} \int_0^\infty y^2 \, e^{-y^2} \, dy$$

$$= \frac{\sqrt{\pi}}{4} \, \xi(\tfrac{3}{2})$$

where $\zeta(\tfrac{3}{2})$ is Riemann's ζ-function and equals $2 \cdot 612$.

Thus

$$n_l = 2 \cdot 612 \left(\frac{2\pi mkT}{h^2}\right)^{3/2}$$

This result should alarm us, since ζ is supposed to be determined by n and T and it now appears that ζ cannot be determined at all if $n > n_l$. The reason is that the sum over energy states which determines n is no longer properly represented by the integral.

Consider the sum

$$\bar{N} = \sum_{i=0}^\infty \frac{1}{\zeta^{-1} \, e^{\alpha_i/kT} - 1}$$

This can take values as large as we please, as ζ tends to $\exp(\alpha_0/kT)$ from below. For simplicity, let us take $\alpha_0 = 0$, shifting the zero of the energy scale from the base of potential energy to the energy of the single-particle ground state. Then the total number n_0 of particles in this ground state is

$$n_0 = (\zeta^{-1} - 1)^{-1}$$

and if we choose $\zeta^{-1} = 1 + (\beta\bar{N})^{-1}$, $0 \leqslant \beta \leqslant 1$

$$n_0 = \beta\bar{N}$$

and we have a fraction β of all the particles present lying down dead in the ground state.

The value of α_1 is now

$$\frac{3h^2}{4m} V^{-2/3}$$

so

$$\frac{\alpha_1}{kT} = \frac{3h^2}{4mkT} V^{-2/3} \sim 9(n_l V)^{-2/3}$$

and the total number of particles in the first excited state is

$$n_1 = \frac{1}{\zeta^{-1} e^{\alpha_1/kT} - 1}$$

$$\doteq \frac{1}{(b\bar{N})^{-1} + 9(n_l V)^{-2/3}}$$

$$\doteq \tfrac{1}{9}(n_l V)^{2/3} \quad \text{for large } \bar{N}$$

since $n_l V$ is of the same order as $\bar{N}$.

Thus $n_1 \sim n_0^{2/3}$, and moreover n_1 is already well enough represented by its value for $\zeta = 1$.

We see, then, that if the number n of particles per unit volume is given, there is a critical temperature T_c defined by

$$n = n_l(T_c)$$

and that for $T < T_c$ we have $n_l(T)$ particles 'live' and distributed over the excited states and a finite fraction, amounting to $n - n_l(T)$ particles, 'dead' in the ground state.

The mean energy of the live particles is easily calculated by the same method used for n_l, but now involves the Riemann $\zeta(\tfrac{5}{2})$ which is 1·341. The mean energy, per particle, of the live particles is then

$$\epsilon = 0 \cdot 5134 \times \tfrac{3}{2}kT$$

and $U \propto T^{5/2}$ for $T < T_c$.

A good deal of labour has been devoted to calculating the behaviour of the Bose–Einstein gas near and below the degeneration temperature, with a view to accounting for the superfluidity of liquid He[4], whose atoms are bosons. It is now evident that an explanation of superfluidity must take account in some detail of the actual forces

3

of interaction between the atoms, which are not at all small in the liquid. However, the isotope He^3, whose atoms are fermions, does not form a superfluid in any conditions yet attained, so the statistics are clearly important as well.

Fermi–Dirac degeneration

In a gas of fermions ζ can take any value, and there is no special physical interest in the point $\zeta = 1$. If ζ is large compared with one, the necessary integrals can be reduced with only moderate exertion (see Appendix, p. 142), to a power series whose first terms are

$$\int_0^\infty \frac{f(x)}{e^{x-a}+1}\,dx = \int_0^a f(x)\,dx + \frac{\pi^2}{6}f'(a) + \frac{7\pi^4}{360}f'''(a) + \cdots$$

Taking the first two terms, we now obtain the numerical density

$$n = C.\tfrac{2}{3}\xi^{3/2}\left[1 + \frac{\pi^2}{8}\left(\frac{kT}{\xi}\right)^2\right]$$

where

$$C = 4\pi(2m/h^2)^{3/2}$$

and

$$\xi = kT\ln\zeta$$

a factor 2 having been included since every energy level may be occupied by two particles of oppositely directed spin (for spin $\tfrac{1}{2}$).

$$C \doteq 3\cdot4 \times 10^{39}\ \text{gm}^{-3/2}\ \text{cm}^{-6}\ \text{sec}^{-3}$$

for particles having the mass of an electron. (The new symbol ξ appears where we should have expected μ. We shall discuss this later.)

Given n and T, this relation can be inverted to find ξ by successive approximations.

The first approximation

$$\xi_0 = \left(\frac{3n}{2C}\right)^{2/3}$$

is the value of ξ exact at $T = 0$. The second approximation—which is as far as we can proceed without including more terms of the original series—is

$$\xi_1 = \xi_0\left[1 - \frac{\pi^2}{12}\left(\frac{kT}{\xi_0}\right)^2\right]$$

The corresponding value of the internal energy per particle is

$$E = \tfrac{3}{5}\xi_0\left(1+\frac{5}{12}\cdot\frac{\pi^2k^2T^2}{\xi_0^2}\right)$$

and the specific heat per particle is therefore

$$C_V = \frac{\pi^2kT}{3\xi_0}\cdot\tfrac{3}{2}k$$

These expressions are in any case valid only for large ξ, i.e. for $\xi \gg kT$, and we see that ξ differs from ξ_0 only by the square of the small quantity kT/ξ_0. In addition, the specific heat is reduced below the equipartition value by a factor roughly $3kT/\xi_0$.

In the degenerate fermion gas, all states which lie much more than kT below the level ξ are fully occupied, and all much more than kT above ξ are empty. By a natural analogy the region of full states is called the Fermi sea; the surface in momentum space corresponding to energy ξ is called the Fermi surface. This surface is a sphere for the gas of perfectly free particles.

The Fermi fluids

There are two important classes of substance whose physical behaviour approximates closely to that of the degenerate ideal gas of fermions. The first is the system of conduction electrons in a metal; the second is the nuclear fluid of which the nuclei of atoms are composed. In each case, the forces of interaction between the particles are very large: however, they apparently average out to provide a potential well equivalent to the box confining an ideal gas.

This effect can be partly understood in terms of a familiar analogy. When a floating body is set in motion in even an non-viscous liquid, the kinetic energy associated with a given speed is greater than the kinetic energy of the floating body alone, since the liquid is also set in motion. The detailed calculation of the energy in the liquid is generally difficult, but there will be a range of speeds over which the flow pattern is unchanging, except that the liquid flow speed is proportional to the speed of the body. In this range, the kinetic energy of the whole system remains proportional to the square of speed, with an effective mass of the order of half as much again or of double the mass of the body.

In a similar way, the lower states of excitation of a Fermi fluid are well described in terms of a 'quasi-particle' which can be visualized as an electron or nucleon moving through the sea of neighbours, along with the connected flow of these neighbours 'cut away before and closing from behind'. Because of the correlated displacement of the neighbours, the quasi-particles interact with each other much less vigorously than do the 'bare' particles in absence of the neighbours.

Conduction of electrons in metals

Once electrons had been identified, towards the end of the last century, it was possible to proceed with some confidence to construct theories of the optical and electrical behaviour of materials in which electron movements played the central role. Such theories had considerable success, but all implied a fundamental difficulty: if electrons can move independently of the atoms to which they are (more or less firmly) attached, then by the well recognized principle of equipartition they should contribute to the specific heat. But, even in metals, Dulong and Petit's law is valid, only the displacements of the atoms as a whole apparently contributing.

This difficulty disappears if the electrons in a metal constitute a Fermi gas which is highly degenerate at ordinary temperatures. To obtain a simple model we first of all abstract from the actual crystalline structure of the material by replacing the ions, which have released the conduction electrons, by a uniform distribution of positive charge; we then suppose that the effect of this charge on the conduction electrons is to mask their mutual repulsion and also to provide a potential well of uniform depth for them to move in. All these steps involve some falsification, but the resulting model, due to Sommerfeld, is surprisingly successful.

One metal contains 3×10^{22} atoms per cc. The value of ξ_0 then, is

$$\left(\frac{3n}{2c}\right)^{2/3} = \left(\frac{9 \times 10^{22}}{2 \times 3 \cdot 4 \times 10^{39}}\right)^{2/3} \text{erg}$$

$$\sim 6 \times 10^{-12} \text{ erg}$$

if we have one conduction electron per atom. This is about 4 eV, whereas kT at room temperature is $\frac{1}{40}$ eV, so these electrons will be contributing about $\frac{1}{50}$ of their equipartition specific heat at room temperature.

At temperatures far below the Debye temperature, however, the specific heat of the crystal lattice vibrations will be varying as T^3, whereas that of the conduction electrons varies as T, so that for T/θ_D less than about $(k\theta_D/\xi_0)^{1/2}/21$ the electron specific heat is the greater of the two. This is verified in practice.

Extending the model

As a result of the regular crystalline structure of a metal, electrons with the appropriate momenta experience Bragg reflection within the metal, and cannot propagate freely. In consequence the energy and momentum are related much less simply than by $E = p^2/2m$. The new relation can be represented by making m a tensor function of k, but fortunately we need only worry about the effect on the density of states as a function of energy. In particular, for a thoroughly degenerate Fermi gas, all we need know is that density and its first few derivatives at ξ_0, in other words, at the surface of the Fermi sea.

Suppose that the number of distinct energy states between E and $E + dE$ is $g(E)\, dE$ before allowing for electron spin. Then each such state may be occupied by two electrons of opposite spin, and the true density of states is $2g(E)$. We then have the relations

$$\bar{N} = 2 \int_0^\infty \frac{g(E)\, dE}{e^{(E-\xi)/kT} + 1}$$

$$U = 2 \int_0^\infty \frac{E\, g(E)\, dE}{e^{(E-\xi)/kT} + 1}$$

which can be reduced, taking E/kT as variable and using the expression on p. 142, to

$$\bar{N} = 2 \int_0^\xi g(E)\, dE + \frac{\pi^2 k^2 T^2}{3}\, g'(\xi)$$

$$U = 2 \int_0^\xi E\, g(E)\, dE + \frac{\pi^2 k^2 T^2}{3}\, (g(\xi) + \xi\, g'(\xi))$$

including only the first two terms of each series.

The value ξ_0 of ξ at $T = 0$ is given by

$$\bar{N} = 2 \int_0^{\xi_0} g(E)\, dE$$

so we have in the next approximation for ξ

$$\xi = \xi_0 - \frac{\pi^2 k^2 T^2}{6} \frac{g'(\xi_0)}{g(\xi_0)}$$

The specific heat is then given in first approximation by

$$\frac{dU}{dT} = \tfrac{2}{3}\pi^2 k^2 T\, g(\xi_0)[1 + O[(kT/\xi_0)^2]]$$

Nuclear fluid

The protons and neutrons of which atomic nuclei are composed are Fermi particles of spin $\tfrac{1}{2}$. It is found that atomic nuclei have a nearly constant density (about 3×10^8 tons per cc), and a nearly constant binding energy per particle. The simplest view of these nuclei is then to treat them as drops of a homogeneous fluid, sometimes called Wignerite in recognition of E. P. Wigner's development of this idea, and, to begin with, to regard Wignerite as a degenerate Fermi gas.

Wignerite contains equal proportions of protons and neutrons, and is not electrically neutral, so that large drops of it are blown apart by their own electric charge. This is why nuclei of mass number above about 240 become unstable against fission. Since protons and neutrons differ in nature although they have almost the same mass, the exclusion principle still permits a given state of translatory motion to be occupied by two protons of opposite spin and two neutrons of opposite spin. Thus the depth of the Fermi sea, ξ_0, in Wignerite of total numerical density ρ is

$$\xi_0 = \frac{h^2}{8m} \left(\frac{3\rho}{2\pi} \right)^{2/3}$$

where m is the neutron or proton mass.

For a spherical nucleus of mass number A the radius r is $r_0 A^{1/3}$, where r_0 is found by electron scattering experiments to be about $1 \cdot 1 \times 10^{-13}$ cm. ξ_0 is proportional to r_0^{-2} and, for the given value of r_0, is 40 MeV. The energy, other than electrostatic, of removing a nucleon (proton or neutron) from the average nucleus is 8 MeV. Thus the Fermi level corresponds to a binding of this amount and the nuclear fluid can be represented as a degenerate Fermi gas in a potential well of depth 48 MeV. This picture leads to a good first approximation to the structure and behaviour of atomic nuclei.

The first excited states of most nuclei lie so high as to have negligible probability of thermal excitation, except in the very high temperatures obtained in nuclear explosions or some electrical discharges. Thermodynamic equilibrium is only approximately attainable in transient conditions, but the idea of equilibrium can be useful even in the very short time-scale of a single nuclear reaction.

'Temperature' in nuclear reactions

While a good deal can be found out about the shape and charge distribution of atomic nuclei by ordinary spectroscopy, that is, from their action on the surrounding electrons, most of our information about their internal structure and motion comes from bombarding them with various fast particles and looking at what comes out. A good deal of what happens can be analysed in terms of a direct interaction between the incident particle and some one particle, or small group, in the nucleus, but there are many events in which the incident particle seems to enter the nucleus and share out the whole of the available energy, forming a compound nucleus at a high level of excitation. This compound nucleus then loses one or more particles by a process analogous to the evaporation of molecules from a hot liquid drop.

The available energy will consist of the kinetic energy of collision (in the centre of mass reference system) plus the binding energy, which is 8 MeV if the incident particle is a nucleon. If this is shared randomly there will be a certain average energy per nucleon which at once enables us to define a corresponding temperature for the Wignerite of the compound nucleus, and to predict the corresponding Maxwell–Boltzmann energy distribution for the particles which ultimately evaporate away. This is verified in many experiments.

We should take note that information is being disregarded in this operation. In the course of a reaction of this sort, total energy and total angular momentum are certainly conserved. Conservation of angular momentum leads to certain angular correlations among incident and emitted particles; these we are neglecting. Conservation of energy leads to strong restrictions on the energy of the emitted particles—for example, if only two particles escape, and there is no radiation, the energy of one implies the energy of the other with an uncertainty which is no more than the uncertainty of experimental measurement. Thus, merely to state a temperature implies that we know less than in fact we do. Nevertheless, this picture has been of real use in the analysis of experimental results.

4

HETEROGENEOUS SYSTEMS

The physical systems for which we have so far calculated thermo-dynamic functions are all of the very simple sort which consist of a single component in a single macroscopic state. As an introduction to heterogeneous systems, let us consider two dissimilar metals in contact, where the condition of equilibrium is equality of chemical potential of the electrons in the two pieces of metal.

Contact potential

The potential energy, and with it the chemical potential, of the electrons in a piece of metal can be shifted up or down by varying the electrical potential of the metal. Let us take the zero of our energy scale to correspond to an electron at rest in air at earth potential. If the depth of the potential well representing the metal is W, we see that the chemical potential of the electrons in the metal at electrical potential V, with respect to the chosen zero, is

$$\mu = \xi + eV - W$$

If now we consider two pieces of metal put into electrical contact so that they can exchange electrons, then in thermodynamic equilibrium

$$\mu_1 = \mu_2$$

i.e.

$$\xi_1 + eV_1 - W_1 = \xi_2 + eV_2 - W_2$$

Note that in these expressions e must be taken as the physical

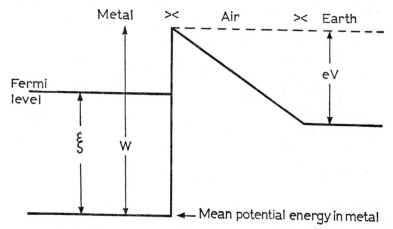

Fig. 2. Fermi level and potential energy distribution for an electron in and near a metal.

charge of the electron, that is, a negative quantity. Thus the situation in the figure corresponds to a negative value of V.

The potential energy W is a function of the density rather than directly of temperature; at constant pressure $\partial W/\partial T$ is small and negative.

The contact potential $V_1 - V_2$ will then depend on temperature mainly through $\xi_2 - \xi_1$, and will vary parabolically with T, with a coefficient depending on the relative rate of variation of density of states with energy at the Fermi surface in each metal.

Notice that this effect, which is not easy to measure, is not the same as the ordinary thermo-electric effect; the latter is due to a dynamical coupling between the flow of heat and the flow of electricity, and this cannot be properly discussed in terms of equilibrium theory.[1]

As usual, there is a limitation of time-scale here. We have supposed that the metals are free only to exchange electrons; over a very long period they would of course exchange atoms as well, and the ultimate equilibrium situation would contain two lumps of alloy (not, in general, of identical composition) such that the chemical potentials of the electrons, and of each sort of metal atom, were each equal in both lumps. Of course, the chemical potentials of the different species would not in general be equal to each other.

[1] Kelvin did as a matter of fact derive correct results in thermo-electricity by a judicious use of equilibrium thermodynamics. His work is now rightly regarded as a foreshadowing of the recently developed subject of irreversible thermodynamics.

This equilibrium between two pieces of solid material is a special case of the problem of phase equilibrium. A phase is a connected region, containing material of uniform or continuously varying density and composition, bounded by a surface at which density or composition change discontinuously. Solid, liquid and vapour of one material, for example, will constitute distinct phases. In a physical system containing several phases, the conditions of thermodynamic equilibrium are uniformity, throughout the system, of temperature, pressure and the chemical potential of each component. We shall now use these conditions, with the results of previous chapters, to study some further equilibria of interest.

Thermionic emission

All metals, when heated in a vacuum, become surrounded by a cloud of negative charge which consists of electrons evaporated out of the metal surface. It is important for the design of thermionic devices to know how the density of this cloud depends on the metal and on the temperature. The distribution of electrons at some distance from the emitting surface depends on the particular electric fields which act on the system, but their concentration just outside the metal surface, provided no net current is flowing, is given simply by the equilibrium condition that the chemical potential of the electrons is the same inside and outside the metal surface.

In terms of the Sommerfeld model which was introduced in the last chapter, we have to equate the chemical potential of a dense electron gas at low potential energy with that of a dilute electron gas at zero potential energy. The metal atoms we regarded as a fixed framework, and their thermal behaviour thus drops out of the problem. We are left with two phases, the interior and exterior of the metal, and one component, the electrons. The chemical potential in each phase is then simply the Gibbs free energy per electron.

For the dense electron gas inside the metal, the chemical potential lies ξ above the potential energy level. With respect to the zero of potential energy, which we choose outside the metal surface, the chemical potential is then

$$\mu = -W + \xi = -\phi$$

and since $\xi \gg kT$, this depends little on temperature. The chemical potential of the electrons in the metal is in fact nearly the total energy of the most energetic electrons at absolute zero: since the electronic specific heat is so small, the effect of entropy in reducing the chemical potential is also small.

For the dilute electron gas outside the metal, the situation is quite different. The Gibbs free energy is

$$G = U + PV - TS \quad \text{by definition}$$

giving

$$\mu = \tfrac{5}{2}kT - TS \quad \text{per electron}$$

i.e.

$$\mu = -kT\left[\ln v + \tfrac{3}{2}\ln\frac{2\pi mkT}{h^2} + \ln 2\right]$$

where v is the volume per electron and we have used the expression derived before for a dilute monatomic gas. The extra term $k\ln 2$ in the entropy arises from the electron spin, whose two values give a total number of quantum states just double the number obtained by considering the translatory motion alone. Since kT is generally much less than ϕ, the important variable is v and the equilibrium condition is obtained essentially by making the density of electrons outside the metal so low that $TS = \phi$. More precisely, we have on equating the values of μ

$$2v\left(\frac{2\pi mkT}{h^2}\right)^{3/2} = e^{\phi/kT}$$

giving for the numerical density n of electrons just outside the metal surface

$$n = 2\left(\frac{2\pi mkT}{h^2}\right)^{3/2} e^{-\phi/kT}$$

and for the pressure which these exert

$$p = (2kT)^{5/2}\left(\frac{\pi m}{h^2}\right)^{3/2} e^{-\phi/kT}$$

Since the electrons are charged, the electron cloud produces an electric field, which can be measured, with some difficulty, to determine n. It is easier to measure the thermionic current which can be drawn away from the metal, as in the ordinary diode valve, by an external electric field. This current saturates as the applied field increases, reaching a maximum density (current per unit area of emitting surface) given by

$$i = AT^2 e^{-b/T}$$

This is connected with the previous expressions by the following argument from kinetic theory.

The number of particles striking unit area in unit time from an ideal gas at pressure p and temperature T is

$$(2\pi mkT)^{-1/2}p$$

Thus the number of electrons falling back on to the metal surface from outside per unit area and time, is

$$f = \frac{4\pi mk^2}{h^3} T^2 \, \mathrm{e}^{-\phi/kT}$$

In the equilibrium situation there is no resultant current away from the metal, so the flux of electrons away from the metal must also be f.

Suppose for simplicity that there is no reflection of electrons on the metal surface. This is reasonable since an electron of charge q at a distance r outside the metal surface experiences an 'image force' attraction $q^2/(4r^2)$ which accelerates it towards the surface, and it is plausible that it will usually lose the kinetic energy thus acquired to the conduction electrons in the metal, and have to await thermal reactivation before it can again escape. (In view of the physical identity of electrons, we express the assumption more properly by saying that the arrival and escape of electrons are uncorrelated events.) Then the flux of electrons away from the metal is controlled only by conditions in and at the surface, and is in particular independent of what is happening in the electron cloud outside the surface.

An external field drawing electrons away from the surface will then decrease the back current of electrons condensing out of the external charge cloud, without affecting the outward flux, and the maximum current density out from the metal surface will be

$$qf = \frac{4\pi mqk^2}{h^3} T^2 \, \mathrm{e}^{-\phi/kT}$$

in agreement with the empirical formula. If some incident electrons are in fact reflected at the metal surface the value of A will be decreased below that, $4\pi mqk^2 h^{-3}$, given by this calculation: otherwise it will depend on the mass and charge of the electron but not on the particular emitting surface, the properties of the material entering only in the determination of ϕ.

The idea used in the last few paragraphs, which is essentially that an equilibrium situation is often profitably described in terms of the balance of two opposite fluxes, is often useful in statistical theory, especially when one wishes to proceed to discuss the non-equilibrium situation as well. We shall meet several other applications of it.

The vapour pressure of a solid

For simplicity, consider first the equilibrium between one of the noble gases and its solid form. There are then no complications such as arise from the internal molecular motions of other substances, and the chemical potential of the gas has its simplest form

$$\mu = -kT \left[\ln v + \frac{3}{2} \ln \frac{2\pi mkT}{h^2} \right]$$

so long as the density is low enough for the gas to be nearly ideal in its behaviour. If that is so, the density of the solid is so high in comparison that the PV term in its Gibbs free energy can be safely neglected, that is, we calculate only the Helmholtz free energy.

This was not worked out above, but it is an easy exercise for the reader to proceed either directly from the partition function or, from the internal energy which we have worked out, via the specific heat and entropy, to obtain the integral which represents the free energy. This needs to be computed numerically for intermediate temperatures, but we can write down good approximations for low and high temperatures, obtaining for μ, with an Einstein model and characteristic temperature E

$$-Q + \tfrac{3}{2}kE \begin{cases} -3kT\,e^{-E/T}, & T \ll E \\ +3kT \ln (E/T), & T \gg E \end{cases}$$

and with a Debye model and characteristic temperature D

$$-Q + \tfrac{9}{8}kD \begin{cases} -3kT\,e^{-D/T} - 19\!\cdot\!5kT^4 D^{-3}, & T \ll D \\ +3kT \ln (D/T) - kT, & T \gg D \end{cases}$$

where Q is the energy of cohesion per molecule—in this case, per atom—and is further considered below.

Vapour pressures are well enough fitted for most purposes by using the Einstein model and the high-temperature form for the free energy. Equating the two expressions for μ in vapour and solid we obtain

$$p = \frac{(2\pi m)^{3/2}}{(kT)^{1/2}} v^3\, e^{-(Q-3kE/2)/kT}$$

where $h\nu = kE$.

We must consider the meaning of Q in more detail. Its definition is that the potential energy of a piece of solid, if all its N atoms were at rest in their equilibrium positions, would be $-NQ$ compared with the energy of these N atoms when all widely separated from each other. It is not the same as the latent heat of evaporation, to which there are other contributions. First of all, each atom in the solid has a base energy, $3kE/2$ above the energy it would have if it could be reduced to rest, due to the zero-point motion: secondly, in its thermal oscillation it has an additional mean potential energy of $3kT/2$, provided the temperature T is much greater than E. Thus the internal energy of evaporation is $Q-(3kE/2)-(3kT/2)$, while the total latent heat of evaporation is $L=Q-(3kE/2)-kT/2$.

To verify that our working is correct we may compare the result with the corresponding expression deduced from Clapeyron's purely thermodynamic relation

$$\frac{\mathrm{d}p}{\mathrm{d}T} = \frac{L}{T\,\Delta v}$$

giving the dependence of equilibrium pressure on temperature for two phases with a heat of transformation L and corresponding volume change Δv. Under the same assumptions as were made at the start of the statistical treatment, Δv, the volume of vapour, is equal to kT/p for each molecule, and L is $L_0-\frac{1}{2}kT$ $(=L_0+p\,\Delta v-3kT/2)$, so

$$\frac{1}{p}\frac{\mathrm{d}p}{\mathrm{d}T} = \frac{L_0-kT/2}{kT^2}$$

and

$$\ln p/p_0 = L_0/kT_0 - L_0/kT + \tfrac{1}{2}\ln(T_0/T)$$

so

$$p = p_0\sqrt{T_0/T}\,\mathrm{e}^{L_0/kT_0}\,\mathrm{e}^{-L_0/kT}$$

giving the same dependence on T as the previous formula. The advantage of the statistical formula is to relate the arbitrary p_0, T_0 to the independently measurable quantities m, ν.

In general, if μ_c is the chemical potential of the condensed phase the equilibrium vapour pressure will be

$$p = \left(\frac{2\pi mkT}{h^2}\right)^{3/2} kT\,\mathrm{e}^{\mu_c/kT}\,\mathrm{e}^{-\Delta\mu/kT}$$

where $\Delta\mu$ is the excess of the vapour phase chemical potential over the simple expression given above. This excess will generally consist of several distinguishable parts. One of these, which will be considered later on, will arise from molecular interactions, corresponding to the deviation of the vapour, at higher pressures, from the ideal gas condition. Others arise from the fact that various degrees of freedom, such as rotation, internal vibration, or electron spin, of the molecule have different ranges of movement in the condensed and vapour phases. Let us separate the contributions μ_c', $\Delta\mu'$ to μ_c and $\Delta\mu$ respectively due to these degrees of freedom. Then

$$\mathrm{e}^{(\mu_c'-\Delta\mu')/kT} = Z_v/Z_c$$

where Z_v and Z_c are the canonical partition functions per molecule in the vapour and condensed phase respectively for the degrees of freedom concerned.

The simplest example is the vapour of an alkali metal. An atom of such a metal has a resultant electron spin angular momentum of $h/4\pi$, which can have two orientations with the same energy in the vapour. In the metal, the electrons couple to give zero net angular momentum, and so, one single state. Hence, as in the thermionic evaporation of electrons themselves, we have $Z_v/Z_c = 2$, and the vapour pressure is twice what one would calculate without allowing for the electron spin.

Again, a polyatomic molecule, such as that of alcohol, may rotate freely in the vapour phase, but be restricted to a narrow range of angular oscillation in the solid or liquid. For methyl alcohol, the corresponding Z_v/Z_c appears to be about 20.[1]

Evaporation and condensation

It is instructive to see how the same vapour pressure equation can be obtained from a kinetic model in which we calculate the rates of condensation and of evaporation and consider the equilibrium pressure at a given temperature as determined by the equality of these two rates. As before, we simplify by neglecting the possibility of reflection for the first round of discussion.

The rate of condensation is again given by

$$f = (2\pi mkT)^{-1/2} p$$

The rate of evaporation is very hard to calculate with a decent degree of rigour, since that would involve a complete discussion of the lattice dynamics of a crystal at the free surface. This has never been done. To obtain a tractable problem we at once adopt the Einstein model, and truncate the question of how energy is transferred among the surface molecules.

A molecule constrained to harmonic oscillation in one dimension will, because of the even density of its states in energy, have a probability $\exp(-W/kT)$ of having a total energy of oscillation of W or more, at temperature T. If we suppose that the sharing of energy among the surface molecules is so rapid that the energy of a given molecule fluctuates widely inside its period of oscillation, the energy distribution for a surface molecule which happens to be

---

[1] This is calculated from the observed vapour pressure and probably includes a contribution from a large change in the vibrations associated with the O—H bonds.

moving outwards will be determined by the oscillator potential in which it is moving, regardless of the possibility of escape which is opening before it. It will then move outwards ν times per second with a probability $\exp(-W/kT)$ on each occasion of having more than the energy W needed for escape. The probability per unit time that it should escape is therefore $\nu \exp(-W/kT)$. One is tempted to put W

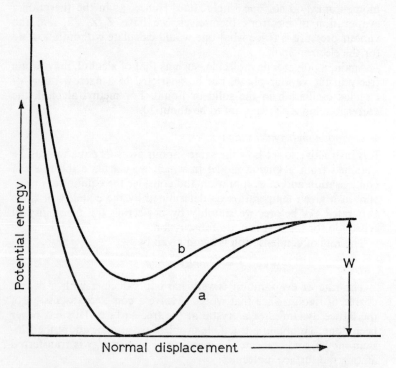

Fig. 3. Variation of potential energy of a surface molecule with displacement normal to the surface, *a*, along the normal through its central position, *b*, along an off-centre normal.

down as the internal heat of vaporization, but this is a little too easy. Besides, it gives the wrong answer, so we must think harder.

Detailed study of the geometry of evaporation from a crystal leads to a series of interesting complications which we cut through with the assumption that all molecules evaporate from a typical situation, such that the energy required to remove a molecule from its equilibrium position in this situation is equal to L_0. However, the molecules vibrate in the plane of the surface as well as normal to it, and a molecule which has some lateral displacement already has a corresponding potential energy, so that the further energy which it requires for escape is reduced below L_0. In fact, a molecule displaced r against a force which makes it oscillate with frequency v has a resulting potential energy $2\pi^2 v^2 m r^2$, and the further energy it needs in order to evaporate is $L_0 - 2\pi^2 v^2 m r^2$.

The probability that a molecule should have a sideways displacement between r and $r + dr$ will be proportional to the area $2\pi r\, dr$ of the ring in which it lies and to the Boltzmann factor $\exp[-2\pi^2 v^2 m r^2 / kT]$ so must be

$$\frac{2\pi r\, e^{-2\pi^2 v^2 m r^2/kT}\, dr}{\int_0^\infty 2\pi r\, e^{-2\pi^2 v^2 m r^2/kT}\, dr}$$

since the probability summed over all r must be unity. Of course, the harmonic force law breaks down for r nearly equal to the molecular spacing, but unless kT is very large this only affects regions where the integrand is already negligible. The integration is easy, giving for this probability

$$\frac{2\pi v^2 m}{kT}\, e^{-2\pi^2 v^2 m r^2/kT}\, 2\pi r\, dr$$

Now the probability of escape per unit time, in the direction normal to the surface, for a molecule with sideways displacement r is

$$v\, e^{-L_0/kT}\, e^{+2\pi^2 v^2 m r^2/kT}$$

so the total probability of escape per unit time for a given molecule is

$$\frac{2\pi v^3 m}{kT}\, e^{-L_0/kT} \int 2\pi r\, dr$$

where $\int 2\pi r\, dr$ is just the area A of surface occupied by the molecule. Thus the rate of evaporation per unit area is

$$\frac{2\pi v^3 m}{kT}\, e^{-L_0/kT}$$

and equating this to the condensation rate

$$(2\pi m kT)^{-1/2} p$$

we obtain for the equilibrium vapour pressure

$$p = \frac{(2\pi m)^{3/2}}{(kT)^{1/2}}\, v^3\, e^{-L_0/kT}$$

an expression identical with that we derived before, using equilibrium statistics. As in the discussion of the thermionic current, the kinetic argument depends on much more detailed assumptions about the process than does the argument from equilibrium statistical mechanics. However, the kinetic argument enables us to estimate the rate of condensation or evaporation when the pressure is maintained above or below its equilibrium value, provided we know the surface temperature.

5

SOME PROBLEMS
BASED ON LINEAR LATTICES

A further important group of soluble problems is concerned with the statistics of linear arrays. They are most directly approached through an attempt to put more realism into the model of a rubber molecule discussed in an earlier chapter (pp. 27–29). To start with, we extend the treatment of the earlier model.

The 'ideal rubber' was dealt with before by evaluating the free energy of the model chain with its ends fixed, and the mean tension in the chain deduced as the derivative of free energy with respect to chain length. An alternative procedure is to build a source of tension into the system being analysed, for example by considering a chain hanging vertically with a weight W on the end. Then a configuration of the chain, of nett length La, will have energy $-WLa$, the potential energy of the weight, associated with it, so that the partition function of the whole system, chain plus weight, becomes

$$\sum_L Z_N(L)\, e^{WLa/kT} \equiv Z_N(W)$$

where L ranges from $-N$ to $+N$ over all integral values of the same parity as N. Since $Z_N(L)$ is simply a binomial coefficient we have

$$Z_N(W) = [e^{Wa/kT} + e^{-Wa/kT}]^N$$
$$= [2 \cosh (Wa/kT)]^N$$

Note that since the chain is allowed only a discrete set of fixed lengths, there is still no way to build the kinetic energy of thermal motion of either chain or weight into the calculation.

To the extent that the corresponding factor of the total partition function, in a more realistic model, may well be independent of L, we shall expect to obtain the right equilibrium length by considering probabilities proportional simply to $Z_N(L) \exp(WLa/kT)$.

Problem: Evaluate the expectation values of L and L^2, given N, W.

The potential energy of the system can, if we wish, be associated with the links of the chain rather than with the weight, thus we obtain exactly the same $Z_N(W)$ if every downward pointing link is given an energy E^- equal to $-Wa$ and every upward pointing link an E^+ equal to $+Wa$, since reversing a link hoists W through a distance $2a$.

The important addition to the model is now to associate an extra energy with the joints of the chain to allow for a certain resistance to bending. In order to gain freedom for further applications of the new model we in fact introduce distinct energies E^{++} associated with the joint between two links of $+$ type, E^{+-} with two links of opposite type, and E^{--} with two links of $-$ type

The statistical discussion now obviously becomes more complicated, for the potential energy of the system depends not only on the total length of the chain but also on the number of points at which reversals occur.

This extended model is effectively identical with that introduced by Ising, and since known by his name, for the discussion of paramagnetic susceptibility. Let us state the problem, then, in its abstract form.

The Ising problem in one dimension

A linear chain of N sites has its state specified when one of two alternative states is assigned to each site. A $+$ state has energy E^+, and a $-$ state has energy E^-, associated with it. Energy E^{++}, E^{--}, E^{+-} is associated with each pair of neighbouring sites according to the states assigned to the sites of the pair. The pairs $+-$ and $-+$ have the same interaction energy E^{+-}.

The number of states of the whole chain for which N^+, the number of $+$ states, and N^R, the number of $+-$ neighbour pairs, are given, can be found by a direct enumeration of possibilities. There is a very neat alternative which is worth using because it foreshadows powerful general results in the study of systems which obey linear mathematical equations. This approach starts by considering the relation between the partition function for a chain of N sites and that for $N+1$ sites.

Some problems based on linear lattices 75

Let the extra site be added at the top end of the chain, regarded as vertically extended. (Of course, any epithet which ensures that we know one end from the other will do.) Since the top site of the N-chain may be either $+$ or $-$, as may the added site, there are four situations to consider:

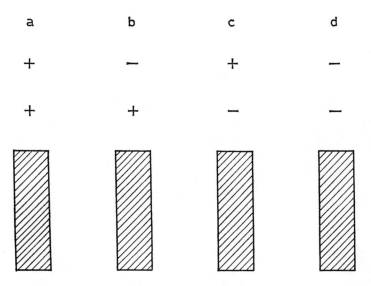

Fig. 4 The four possible configurations of two terminal sites on an Ising chain.

Any detailed analysis of what goes on in the lower part of the chain leads to unprofitable complication at this stage. Instead, suppose that the partition function Z_N for the N-chain is written as

$$Z_N = Z_N^+ + Z_N^-$$

where Z_N^+ is the p.f. for a chain whose top site is known to be in a $+$ state, Z_N^- for a chain whose top site is known to be in a $-$ state, and consider the relation of the Z^+ and Z^- for chains of different N.

Z_{N+1}^+ is a sum over the states which appear in situations a and c above. Correspondingly, Z_{N+1}^- is obtained from situations b and d. Thus

$$Z_{N+1}^+ = Z_N^+ \, e^{-(E^+ + E^{++})/kT} + Z_N^- \, e^{-(E^+ + E^{+-})/kT}$$
$$Z_{N+1}^- = Z_N^+ \, e^{-(E^- + E^{+-})/kT} + Z_N^- \, e^{-(E^- + E^{--})/kT}$$

so that $Z_{N+1}^{+},{}_{1}^{-}$ are linear combinations of $Z_N^{+},{}^{-}$ with coefficients which do not depend on N. If Z_N^{+}, Z_N^{-} are considered as components of a vector quantity, the above pair of equations can be written formally

$$\begin{bmatrix} Z_{N+1}^{+} \\ Z_{N+1}^{-} \end{bmatrix} = [M] \begin{bmatrix} Z_N^{+} \\ Z_N^{-} \end{bmatrix}$$

where

$$[M] = \begin{bmatrix} e^{-\beta(E^{+}+E^{++})} & e^{-\beta(E^{+}+E^{+-})} \\ e^{-\beta(E^{-}+E^{+-})} & e^{-\beta(E^{-}+E^{--})} \end{bmatrix}$$

and $\beta = 1/kT$. The equation is now in matrix form, but for our purpose this structure can simply be regarded as shorthand for the preceding pair of equations. The new notation has the advantage of directing attention to the operator $[M]$ as much as to the Z. If we interpret $[M]^n$ as the performance of the operation $[M]$, n times in succession, it is evident that

$$\begin{bmatrix} Z_{N+1}^{+} \\ Z_{N+1}^{-} \end{bmatrix} = [M]^N \begin{bmatrix} Z_1^{+} \\ Z_1^{-} \end{bmatrix}$$

$$= [M]^N \begin{bmatrix} e^{-\beta E^{+}} \\ e^{-\beta E^{-}} \end{bmatrix}$$

Again, if we interpret $a[M]$ as 'following the operation $[M]$ by multiplying both results by a', and $[M/a]$ as the operator obtained by dividing every element of $[M]$ by a, it is evident that $[M] = a[M/a]$, so that the particular $[M]$ which concerns us can be written

$e^{-\frac{1}{2}\beta(E^{+}+E^{-}+E^{++}+E^{--})}$

$$\times \begin{bmatrix} e^{-\frac{1}{2}\beta(E^{+}-E^{-}+E^{++}-E^{--})} & e^{-\frac{1}{2}\beta(E^{+}-E^{-}+2E^{+-}-E^{++}+E^{--})} \\ e^{-\frac{1}{2}\beta(E^{-}-E^{+}+2E^{+-}-E^{++}+E^{--})} & e^{-\frac{1}{2}\beta(E^{-}-E^{+}+E^{--}-E^{++})} \end{bmatrix}$$

or

$$[M] = a \begin{bmatrix} b & c\,e^{-\beta A} \\ c^{-1}\,e^{-\beta A} & b^{-1} \end{bmatrix} \equiv a[M']$$

where

$$-\ln a = \tfrac{1}{2}\beta(E^{+}+E^{-}+E^{++}+E^{--})$$
$$-\ln b = \tfrac{1}{2}\beta(E^{+}-E^{-}+E^{++}-E^{--})$$
$$-\ln c = \tfrac{1}{2}\beta(E^{+}-E^{-})$$
$$A = E^{+-}-\tfrac{1}{2}(E^{++}+E^{--})$$

Then $[M]^N = a^N[M']^N$, and the symmetry of $[M']$ makes it a slightly more tractable object than $[M]$.

It is clear that if a pair of numbers x, y exists such that

$$[M'] \begin{bmatrix} x \\ y \end{bmatrix} = \begin{bmatrix} mx \\ my \end{bmatrix} = m \begin{bmatrix} x \\ y \end{bmatrix}$$

then

$$[M']^N \begin{bmatrix} x \\ y \end{bmatrix} = m^N \begin{bmatrix} x \\ y \end{bmatrix}$$

Let us examine this possibility.

Evidently

$$[M'] \begin{bmatrix} x \\ y \end{bmatrix} = m \begin{bmatrix} x \\ y \end{bmatrix}$$

is the same relation as

$$\begin{bmatrix} b-m & c\,e^{-\beta A} \\ c^{-1}\,e^{-\beta A} & b^{-1}-m \end{bmatrix} \begin{bmatrix} x \\ y \end{bmatrix} = 0$$

which when written out gives two distinct equations determining x/y. If the two values of x/y coincide, the equations are consistent, and the condition for this is

$$(b-m)(b^{-1}-m) = e^{-2\beta A}$$

that is

$$[m - \tfrac{1}{2}(b+b^{-1})]^2 = e^{-2\beta A} + \tfrac{1}{4}(b-b^{-1})^2$$

or

$$m = \tfrac{1}{2}(b+b^{-1}) \pm [\tfrac{1}{4}(b-b^{-1})^2 + e^{-2\beta A}]^{1/2}$$

so the relation can be satisfied for two values of m and two corresponding ratios of x to y, which are in fact given by

$$\frac{x}{y} = \frac{c\,e^{-\beta A}}{m-b}$$

If we call the larger and smaller value of m, m_1 and m_2 respectively, and call the corresponding values of x/y, x_1/y_1 and x_2/y_2 respectively, the choice of actual values of x_1 and x_2 is arbitrary, but y_1 and y_2 are then defined. Having chosen x_1, x_2 we can then write

$$Z_1^+ = fx_1 + gx_2$$
$$Z_1^- = fy_1 + gy_2$$

and determine f and g. Notice that since x_2/y_2 is negative, whereas Z_1^+/Z_1^- is positive, f is never zero.

Then

$$[M]^N \begin{bmatrix} Z_1^+ \\ Z_1^- \end{bmatrix} = a^N [M']^N \left\{ f \begin{bmatrix} x_1 \\ y_1 \end{bmatrix} + g \begin{bmatrix} x_2 \\ y_2 \end{bmatrix} \right\}$$

$$= a^N m_1^N f \begin{bmatrix} x_1 \\ y_1 \end{bmatrix} + a^N m_2^N g \begin{bmatrix} x_2 \\ y_2 \end{bmatrix}$$

so

$$Z_{N+1} = a^N [m_1^N f(x_1 + y_1) + m_2^N g(x_2 + y_2)]$$

If we are interested, as is usually the case, only in the limiting behaviour of the system for large N, then the fact that $m_1 > m_2$ leads to the very simple result

$$\lim_{N \to \infty} N^{-1} \ln Z_N = \ln (am_1)$$

Applications

The Ising problem can be interpreted as representing several distinct physical situations, by suitable choice of the energy parameters appearing in it.

(i) *Ideal rubber.* As indicated above, we set $E^+ = Wa$, $E^- = -Wa$, and it is reasonable to set $E^{++} = E^{--} = 0$, $E^{+-} = A$. In this case, then

$$a = 1, \qquad b = c = e^{-Wa/kT}$$

and

$$m_1 = \cosh (Wa/kT) + [e^{-2A/kT} + \sinh^2 (Wa/kT)]^{1/2}$$

(ii) *Magnet.* If we now consider a chain of magnetic dipoles in an external field H, permitting the dipoles only the alternative alignments parallel or antiparallel to the field, the energy of reversing one dipole by itself is $E^+ - E^- = 2mH$, where m is the moment of the dipole. The physical interaction of the dipoles with each other includes of course the effect on each of them of the magnetic field due to its neighbours, but this is completely dominated in ferro-magnetic or antiferromagnetic substances by an electrostatic inter-action between the magnetic electrons on neighbouring atoms. This interaction depends indirectly on whether the electron spins are parallel or antiparallel, and the electron spin on each atom deter-mines its magnetic moment. A not unreasonable model for the real magnet is then obtained by setting $E^{++} = E^{--} = -J$, $E^{+-} = J$, where J is positive for a ferromagnet, in which neighbouring spins set parallel at low temperatures, while it is negative for an antiferro-magnet, whose ordered state at low temperature contains anti-parallel neighbours.

(iii) *Lattice gas.* The adsorption of gas molecules on a solid surface, or of solute molecules along a linear polymer chain, gives rise to situations which can be represented in terms of an Ising model.

Consider a long-chain molecule which provides N similar sites for the attachment of a smaller molecule whose chemical potential is μ. For simplicity, suppose that no other chemical species is present. The grand partition function for the adsorbed molecules is then

$$\sum_{N^+ = 0}^{N} e^{N^+ \mu/kT} q^{N^+} g(N^+, s, N) e^{-(N^+ E + sB)/kT}$$

where N^+ is the number of adsorbed molecules, q the partition function for the motion of one molecule on a lattice site, assumed independent of the presence of a neighbour, E the energy of an adsorbed molecule in its equilibrium position, B the energy associated with two molecules adsorbed on adjacent sites, s the number of such pairs, and g the number of configurations then possible for the N^+ molecules. This can be rewritten as

$$\sum e^{-N^+ (E - \mu - kT \ln q)/kT} e^{-sB/kT} g$$

and it is evident that this is the partition function for the Ising problem if we set

$$E^+ = E - \mu - kT \ln q$$
$$E^{++} = B$$
$$E^- = E^{+-} = E^{--} = 0$$

Here $a = b$ and

$$-\ln a = \frac{1}{2kT} (E + B - \mu - kT \ln q)$$

$$-\ln c = \frac{1}{2kT} (E - \mu - kT \ln q)$$

$$A = -\tfrac{1}{2} B$$

In this case

$$m_1 = \cosh [(E + B - \mu - kT \ln q)/2kT]$$
$$+ [e^{+B/kT} + \sinh^2 [(E + B - a - kT \ln q)/2kT]]^{1/2}$$

and for the very simple situation where $B = 0$ we have

$$a = q^{1/2} e^{(\mu - E)/2kT}$$
$$m_1 = 2 \cosh [(E - \mu - kT \ln q)/2kT]$$

and

$$N^{-1} \ln Z_N \sim \tfrac{1}{2} \ln q + \frac{\mu - E}{2kT} + \ln m_1$$

Here we are interested in $\overline{N^+}$, which is evidently

$$Z_N^{-1} q \frac{\partial Z_N}{\partial q} = \frac{\partial \ln Z_N}{\partial \ln q}$$

so

$$\overline{N^+}/N = \tfrac{1}{2} + \tfrac{1}{2} \tanh \left[(kT \ln q + \mu - E)/2kT \right]$$

If we consider the behaviour of $\overline{N^+}/N$ at fixed temperature when μ is varied, this runs from zero at large negative μ to unity at large positive μ. Half cover of the adsorber is reached when $\mu = E - kT \ln q$.

When μ is expressed in terms of concentration or pressure in a bulk phase (solution or vapour) in equilibrium with the adsorbing surface, the corresponding expression for $\overline{N^+}/N$ is known as an adsorption isotherm. Of particular interest is the expression for μ in terms of the pressure of an equivalent ideal gas, since this is often a nearly correct expression in terms of the actual saturation vapour pressure. We have

$$\mu = -kT \left[\ln \frac{kT}{p} + \frac{3}{2} \ln \frac{2\pi mkT}{h^2} + \ln \mathscr{R}\mathscr{V} \right]$$

where $\mathscr{R}, \mathscr{V}$ are factors in the partition function for the rotation and internal vibrations of the molecule. This gives the very simple isotherm

$$\overline{N^+}/N = \tfrac{1}{2} + \tfrac{1}{2} \tanh \left[a(T) + \tfrac{1}{2} \ln p \right]$$

In this case, with $B = 0$, the non-interacting molecules are distributed entirely at random over the N adsorbing sites. For non-zero B, there is a tendency to crowding or spacing according to the sign of B, but the simple functional form of Z_N cannot produce any phase transition, such as is known to occur in two-dimensional systems (surface melting).

(iv) *Competing adsorption—linear solution.* If two different types of molecule compete for the same chain of adsorption sites, each site has three possible situations; occupied by a $+$ molecule, occupied by a $-$ molecule, or vacant. The method of analysis used above is directly applicable to this problem, but identifying the three values of m arising from a three-square matrix involves solving a cubic equation.

The problem reduces to the case already solved if we take the chemical potentials of both types of molecule to be comparable, but so high that the configurations containing vacant lattice sites are negligibly probable. The choice of parameters in the Ising problem is evidently

$$E^+ = V^+ - \mu^+ - kT \ln q^+$$
$$E^- = V^- - \mu^- - kT \ln q^-$$

while E^{++}, E^{+-}, E^{--} represent the interaction energies.

Here V^+, V^- are energies in the equilibrium positions, corresponding to E in the lattice gas problem. The energy $A = E^{+-} - \frac{1}{2}(E^{++} + E^{--})$ is a measure of the energetic preference for forming bonds between like rather than unlike neighbours.

If we consider how the distribution of molecules varies with temperature, while μ^+ and μ^- are adjusted so as to keep N^+ and N^- constant and each equal to $N/2$, we see that the distribution will be entirely random at very high temperature, and will depend on the sign of A at very low temperature. If A is positive, the configuration of lowest energy contains $N/2$ molecules of one type followed by $N/2$ of the other with only one dissimilar neighbour pair. The energy of this configuration of complete segregation is

$$\frac{N}{2}(V^+ + V^-) + \left(\frac{N}{2} - 1\right)E^{++} + \left(\frac{N}{2} - 1\right)E^{--} + E^{+-}$$

If A is negative the configuration of lowest energy consists of an alternating chain in which only dissimilar neighbour pairs occur. The energy of this completely ordered configuration is

$$\frac{N}{2}(V^+ + V^-) + (N-1)E^{+-}$$

The energy of the segregated state is higher than that of the ordered state by

$$(N-2)\left(\frac{E^{++}}{2} + \frac{E^{--}}{2} - E^{+-}\right)$$

i.e.

$$-(N-2)A$$

In the limit of large N then, A is the energy per molecule to be gained by forming the segregated state from the ordered one. Energy $-A$ is gained by ordering, and if A itself is negative then $-A$ is frequently called the ordering energy.

Where E^{++}, E^{--}, E^{+-} are negative, a stable linear chain, a co-polymer or linear solid solution, may be formed without an adsorbing base. The thermodynamics of this situation follow then simply by setting $V^+ = V^- = 0$.

The Bethe method

The treatment of the one-dimensional Ising problem, given in the first part of this chapter, is unfortunately difficult to extend to two dimensions. In fact the Ising problem for a two-dimensional network has only been solved (originally by Onsager) for the restricted situation with $E^+ = E^-$; and no complete solution has yet been found for any case of the Ising problem in three dimensions.

An alternative approach to the Ising problem, which gives the exact result in one dimension and gives rise to useful simple approximations in two and three dimensions, is due to Bethe. There are two essential steps in Bethe's method. First of all, the extensive physical object to be studied is separated into a small system, which is described precisely, and an environment, whose properties are described by a parameter; secondly, a consistency condition permits the evaluation of this parameter in terms of the initial conditions of the problem.

We have already seen, in the notation of the previous section,

$$\begin{aligned} Z_{N+1} &= Z_{N+1}^+ + Z_{N+1}^- \\ &= e^{-E^+/kT} \left(e^{-E^{++}/kT} Z_N^+ + e^{-E^{+-}/kT} Z_N^- \right) \\ &\quad + e^{-E^-/kT} \left(e^{-E^{+-}/kT} Z_N^+ + e^{-E^{--}/kT} Z_N^- \right) \end{aligned}$$

which we can recognize as a particular case of

$$Z_{\mathrm{I+II}} = \sum_{C_1} e^{-E(C_1)/kT} e^{-F_2(C_1)/kT}$$

where C_1 is a distinct state of a system I, I is coupled to an environment II, and $F_2(C_1)$ is the free energy of the environment under the constraint that I is in state C_1. In the particular application, I is the $(N+1)$th site and II is the rest of the chain. Note that the energy of interaction between I and II is incorporated in F_2.

If the system I contains several adjacent sites, the value of F_2 will depend only on the states of those sites in I which are immediate neighbours of sites in II. We now apply the method with a more fruitful choice of I, taking this to consist of three typical adjacent sites somewhere in the interior of the chain. II falls into two completely independent parts, L and R say, and there are eight distinct C_1 to consider. We examine the relative probability of these C_1. Since L and R are independent we have

$$Z_{\mathrm{I+II}} = \sum_{C_1} e^{-E(C_1)/kT} e^{-F_L(C_1)/kT} e^{-F_R(C_1)/kT}$$

and

$$p(C_1) = e^{-[E(C_1) + F_L(C_1) + F_R(C_1)]/kT} / Z_{I+II}$$

where $F_L(C_1)$ takes only two values $F_L(+)$ and $F_L(-)$ according as the adjacent site in I is in state $+$ or $-$. Similarly, $F_R(C_1)$ takes only values $F_R(+)$ and $F_R(-)$.

Now suppose that L and R are both so large that

$$F_L(+) - F_L(-) = F_R(+) - F_R(-)$$

independent of the size of L and R. Then $p(C_1)$ depends only on the state of the central site of I and the number (0, 1 or 2) of $+$ states on the two outer sites. Thus

$$\frac{n!(2-n)!}{2} p(+, n) = qz^n e^{-[(n+1)E^+ + nE^{++} + (2-n)E^{+-} + (2-n)E^-]/kT}$$

$$\frac{n!(2-n)!}{2} p(-, n) = qz^n e^{-[nE^+ + (2-n)E^{--} + nE^{+-} + (3-n)E^-]/kT}$$

where q is determined so as to normalize the set of probabilities p, by making their sum unity.

The parameter z can now be determined by the following ingenious device. The expectation number of $+$ states on a typical site must be

$$\sum_n p(+, n)$$

The expectation number of $+$ neighbours of a typical site must be

$$\sum_n n[p(+, n) + p(-, n)]$$

For these two statements to be consistent we require

$$\sum_n n[p(+, n) + p(-, n)] = 2 \sum_n p(+, n)$$

i.e.

$$2p(-, 2) + p(-, 1) - p(+, 1) = 2p(+, 0)$$

which is a quadratic equation in z with one positive root and one negative. The negative root fails to meet the condition that $p(\pm, 1)$ must remain positive, so z is uniquely defined.

It will be convenient to contract the notation so that

$$\tfrac{1}{2} n!(2-n)! p(+, n) = qz^n e^{-\beta(E^+ + 2E^{+-})} e^{-\beta n(E^{++} - E^{+-})}$$

$$\equiv qz^n \, \delta y^n$$

and
$$\tfrac{1}{2}n!(2-n)!\,p(-,n) = qz^n\,\mathrm{e}^{-\beta(E^-+2E^{--})}\,\mathrm{e}^{-\beta n(E^{+-}-E^{--})}$$
$$\equiv qz^n\gamma x^n$$

where
$$y = ax, \qquad a = \mathrm{e}^{-\beta(E^{++}+E^{--}-2E^{+-})} = \mathrm{e}^{2\beta A}$$

and other factors have been incorporated in z and q.

Then the equation defining z is
$$z^2\gamma x^2 + z\gamma x - z\delta y = \delta$$

or
$$\gamma zx(1+zx) = \delta(1+zy)$$

The second form is not useful in solving for z, but convenient for some other operations.

The value of z is evidently
$$\frac{1}{2x}\left[\left(\frac{\delta y}{\gamma x}-1\right)+\left(4x^2\delta+\left(\frac{\delta y}{\gamma x}-1\right)^2\right)^{1/2}\right]$$

which then defines the values of the p.

The quasi-chemical equation

A useful and elegant relation can now be had for the probabilities of the different bond types.

A given site can only have $(++)$ bonds radiating from it if it is in a $+$ state and has at least one $+$ neighbour. The expectation number of $(++)$ bonds in which it shares is
$$2n^{++} = 2p(+,2)+p(+,1)$$

so that the probability n^{++} that a given bond is of $(++)$ type is given by
$$n^{++} = q\delta(z^2y^2+zy)$$

Similarly
$$n^{--} = q\gamma(1+zx)$$

and
$$n^{+-} = q(\delta+\delta zy+\gamma z^2x^2+\gamma zx)$$
$$= 2q\delta(1+zy)$$

Thus
$$\frac{(n^{+-})^2}{4n^{++}n^{--}} = \frac{\delta^2(1+zy)^2}{\delta zy(1+zy)\gamma(1+zx)}$$
$$= \frac{x}{y}\frac{\delta(1+zy)}{\delta zx(1+zx)}$$
$$= \frac{x}{y} = \mathrm{e}^{-2\beta A}$$

The formal resemblance between this result and the mass action law for a reaction $A_2 + B_2 \rightleftharpoons 2AB$ has led to the former being named the quasi-chemical equation.

Problem: The energy associated with a lattice site in any particular configuration is the energy of the state at that site plus half the energy of the bonds radiating from it. (The other half belongs to the sites at the other ends of these bonds.) Calculate the expectation value of the energy for a typical site, and show that this agrees with the value obtained from the previously calculated partition function.

Since the Bethe method already gives the exact result for the problem to which we have applied it, there is no point in generalizing to a larger system I than has been used. Moreover, the same correct result would have been obtained by postulating the quasi-chemical equation as the starting point of the calculation. However, the use of the Bethe method in one dimension involves one fact and one assumption, neither of which extends to two or three dimensions. The fact is that L and R are completely independent of each other because they are completely disconnected by the interposed group of 3 sites. The assumption (which we know is right because of our prior matrix calculation) is that, for large L, $F_L(+)/F_L(-)$ becomes independent of the size of L. In a system in which long-range order existed, this ratio would still alternate, as the number of sites in L was even or odd, even for large L.

Thus in using the Bethe method in two- or three-dimensional lattices, the possibility of the correct type of long-range order must be built in at the start, by distinguishing the sub-lattices involved. This is easy enough to do correctly, knowing the natural phenomena, and we return to this later (pp. 106–117). The other, worse, difficulty is that a compact system I in the interior of the lattice is surrounded by a single connected system II so that the introduction of the same factor z^n for n surface sites, independent of their arrangement, is in general wrong. It turns out that the assumption of the quasi-chemical equation is equivalent to the Bethe method only when I consists of a central site and the set of its immediate neighbours. The Bethe method can sometimes be improved by a more elaborate choice of I, but the calculations rapidly become involved.

6

MOLECULAR INTERACTIONS IN GASES

We have seen in the last chapter how to deal with particles having a particularly simple interaction, described by a single energy constant, in the particular problem of linear adsorption. The Bethe, or the quasi-chemical, approximation gives an approach to the behaviour of the corresponding 'lattice gas' in two or three dimensions, and this problem will be reconsidered later (pp. 101–106).

The interactions of atoms and molecules cannot in general be so summarily described. Since the existence and relations of the various states of matter depend on these interactions we must consider them now with more care. The simplest to describe, but by no means the simplest to calculate with, is the Coulomb interaction between charged particles. We shall leave this for later consideration (pp. 135–140).

Neutral atoms and non-polar molecules, then, have the following interactions. At long range, there is a rapidly fluctuating mutual polarization giving rise to an attractive potential energy varying as the inverse sixth power of the separation; this is the potential of the dispersion or van der Waals forces. At short range there may be a covalent binding energy varying roughly as an exponential function of the distance, $\exp(-r/a)$, with a decay length a usually of one or two Ångströms. At very short range there is a strong repulsion, varying usually as a rapid exponential or a high inverse power (ten- or twelve-fold) of the distance. This repulsion arises from the Pauli exclusion principle which prevents the interpenetration of the wave functions representing the inner electron shells of the atoms. In the hydrogen molecule, where alone these inner shells are absent, the repulsion is merely the Coulomb repulsion of the hydrogen nuclei.

A difficulty which is always present in principle is that the inter-action of two bodies must be affected by the presence of a third, since the third acting on the others deforms each of them and so changes their action on each other. 'Many-body' interactions of this sort are usually disregarded for the operation of the van der Waals attractions, with good justification, and for the overlap repulsion, with rather less justification: they are never negligible for covalent interactions.

Covalent binding shows the particular characteristic of saturation. For example, two hydrogen atoms bind strongly to form a molecule. A third atom interacts much less strongly with the molecule. Two molecules interact with each other even less strongly.

Let us consider, then, two extreme models. One represents in a simplified way the dissociation of a covalently bound diatomic mole-cule. We assume a strong interaction between atoms which are bound in a molecule, none between atoms and molecules, and, rather inconsistently, none between free atoms. What we really require is just enough interaction to make recombination possible, but not enough to disturb the equation of state.

The other extreme model is one in which the potential energy of interaction of any two particles is quite independent of the presence of any others. This is quite a good model for the monatomic rare gases, and for many other substances under conditions where no dissociation occurs.

Dissociation equilibrium in a gas

Suppose that in a volume V we have enough material to constitute N molecules of a compound C, which is partly dissociated by a reaction whose chemical equation is

$$\gamma C = \alpha A + \beta B$$

An example might be

$$2NH_3 = N_2 + 3H_2$$

If we have in fact $N_C = N - \gamma M$ molecules of C present we shall have $N_A = \alpha M$ molecules of A and $N_B = \beta M$ of B. Treating the species A, B and C as interpenetrating, independent hot dilute ideal gases, the partition function for the system becomes

$$Z(N, M, V, T) = \frac{1}{(N-\gamma M)!} \left(\frac{Vq_C}{\Lambda_C^3}\right)^{N-\gamma M}$$
$$\times \frac{1}{(\alpha M)!} \left(\frac{Vq_A}{\Lambda_A^3}\right)^{\alpha M} \times \frac{1}{(\beta M)!} \left(\frac{Vq_B}{\Lambda_B^3}\right)^{\beta M}$$

4

and the corresponding Helmholtz free energy F is given by

$$-\frac{F}{kT} = (N-\gamma M)\left(1+\ln\frac{Vq_C}{(N-\gamma M)\Lambda_C^3}\right)$$
$$+\alpha M\left(1+\ln\frac{Vq_A}{\alpha M\Lambda_A^3}\right)+\beta M\left(1+\ln\frac{Vq_B}{\beta M\Lambda_B^3}\right)$$

so that the equilibrium condition for given N, V, T is obtained by maximizing this expression with respect to M to yield

$$\gamma\ln\frac{Vq_C}{N_C\Lambda_C^3} = \alpha\ln\frac{Vq_A}{N_A\Lambda_A^3}+\beta\ln\frac{Vq_B}{N_B\Lambda_B^3}$$

Problem: Verify the derivation, and that the result is equivalent to $\gamma\mu_C=\alpha\mu_A+\beta\mu_B$, which is the thermodynamic equilibrium condition. The thermodynamic condition is true, of course, for reactants in any physical state.

Notice that if the energy values used in calculating q_A and q_B are reckoned from the state where A and B are at rest at a distance from other objects, the energy zero for q_C is at $-E_C$ where γE_C is the reduction of energy on assembling α, A and β, B into γ, C molecules likewise at rest. Thus $q_C=q_C'\exp(E_c/kT)$ where q_C' is reckoned on a similar basis to q_A and q_B.

The equilibrium condition in another form is

$$\frac{N_C^\gamma}{N_A^\alpha N_B^\beta} = V^{\gamma-\alpha-\beta}\frac{\Lambda_A^{3\alpha}\Lambda_B^{3\beta}}{\Lambda_C^{3\gamma}}\frac{q_C^\gamma}{q_A^\alpha q_B^\beta}$$

$$\equiv K(T), \quad \text{an 'equilibrium' constant;}$$

or

$$N_C^\gamma = KN_A^\alpha N_B^\beta$$

which expresses the law of mass action for this particular process. Alternatively

$$N-\gamma M = (K\alpha^\alpha\beta^\beta M^{\alpha+\beta})^{1/\gamma}$$

For the dissociation of a diatomic gas, or for the example of ammonia, quoted above, $(\alpha+\beta)/\gamma=2$, and the equilibrium condition is a quadratic. For the general case, numerical solution is easy. Near the limits of complete dissociation and complete association, we can iterate, as follows.

For complete dissociation, $N_c=0$, i.e.

$$N = \gamma M_0$$

and the next approximation for nearly complete dissociation is to put this M_0 into the other side of the equilibrium condition, to obtain

$$\gamma M_1 = N - (K\alpha^\alpha\beta^\beta M_0^{\alpha+\beta})^{1/\gamma}$$
$$\gamma M_2 = N - (K\alpha^\alpha\beta^\beta M_1^{\alpha+\beta})^{1/\gamma}$$

and so on.

For complete association $M_0 = 0$, and the next approximation is to take $N_0 = N$ in the equilibrium condition, so that

$$K\alpha^\alpha\beta^\beta M_1^{\alpha+\beta} = N^\gamma$$
$$K\alpha^\alpha\beta^\beta M_2^{\alpha+\beta} = (N - \gamma M_1)^\gamma$$

and so on.

The temperature dependence of K is completely dominated by $\exp(\gamma E_C/kT)$ in most circumstances. It retains a volume dependence through the term $V^{\gamma-\alpha-\beta}$, so that at given temperature one will always have complete dissociation at low enough density, but it is easy to see that for a dissociation energy of several electron volts dissociation will be nearly complete only at the density of interstellar space.

Atom interchange

One interesting example of a reaction equilibrium is the exchange

$$2AB = AA + BB$$

corresponding to $\gamma = 2$, $\alpha = \beta = 1$, so that at equilibrium

$$\frac{N_{AB}^2}{N_{AA}N_{BB}} = \left(\frac{\Lambda_{AA}\Lambda_{BB}}{\Lambda_{AB}^2}\right)^3 \frac{q_{AB}^2}{q_{AA}q_{BB}}$$

with the temperature dependent right-hand side dominated by $\exp[\beta(E_{AA} + E_{BB} - 2E_{AB})]$ where $E_{\alpha\beta}$ is the energy of the molecule $\alpha\beta$ at rest measured from the energy of the separated atoms at rest. The energy $-\frac{1}{2}(E_{AA} + E_{BB} - 2E_{AB})$ is the energy per molecule of AB required to make AB from AA and BB.

Bimolecular association

Another special case, $\gamma = 1$, $\alpha = 2$, $\beta = 0$ is of particular interest. At the high association limit it is relevant to equilibria such as $H_2 = H + H$ and at the high dissociation limit it gives a first-order model of the equilibrium $(H_2)_2 = H_2 + H_2$ between pairs and single molecules in gas not far from condensation. The values of E_C for these two situations differ by a factor of over 100.

If we put $n_C = N_C/V$ and $N_A = N_A/V$, the equilibrium condition is

$$\frac{n_C}{n_A^2} = \frac{\Lambda_A^6}{\Lambda_C^3} \frac{q_C}{q_A^2} = K$$

where

$$n_C = n - n_A/2$$

so

$$n - \tfrac{1}{2}n_A = Kn_A^2 \quad \text{and} \quad n_A = \frac{1}{4K}(\sqrt{1 + 16nK} - 1)$$

Which way to expand the square root depends on the value of K. If that is very small ($16nK \ll 1$)

$$n_A \doteq 2n - 8n^2K + 64n^3K^2 + \cdots$$
$$n_C = \qquad 4n^2K - 32n^3K^2 - \cdots$$

and

$$p = (n_A + n_C)kT \quad \text{(assuming ideal behaviour)}$$
$$= 2nkT(1 - 2Kn + 16K^2n^2 + \cdots)$$

The development of the pressure as a power series in the numerical density is a well-known representation for the equation of state of an imperfect gas. The natural variable to use is the total number of molecules of monomer present, which is $m = 2n$, so we have for our model

$$p = mkT(1 - Km + 4K^2m^2 + \cdots)$$

Comparing this with the usual notation

$$p = mkT(1 + bm + cm^2 + \cdots)$$

we see that the model predicts

$$b < 0, \quad c = 4b^2$$

The Van der Waals equation of state, rearranged into the form of the virial expansion, agrees in giving a positive third coefficient, c, but no necessary relation between the third and second coefficients. Indeed, when the experimentally determined equations of state of various gases are expressed in virial form it appears that the second coefficient b is normally negative at low and positive at high temperatures.

Evidently, the use of a mathematical model founded on saturating forces, to fit a situation where the forces certainly do not saturate, is decidedly optimistic. Something better has to be found.

Independently interacting molecules—Van der Waals equation

We now consider molecular interactions such that two molecules, i and j say, have a potential energy of mutual interaction ϕ_{ij} which depends on their separation and relative orientation, but not on the presence of other neighbouring molecules. For a collection of N such molecules numbered by subscripts $1, 2, \ldots, N$, the total potential energy is just the sum of the two body potentials

$$\mathscr{V} = \sum_{i > j} \phi_{ij}$$

care being taken to write the expression so that no particle interacts with itself and no term is included twice over.

For atoms, atomic ions, and sufficiently spherical molecules, ϕ_{ij} depends only on the distance r_{ij} between molecular centres, and we may write

$$\mathscr{V} = \sum_{i > j} \phi(r_{ij})$$

where ϕ is the same function for all pairs if all molecules belong to the same chemical species. Thus for a pure substance the partition function for N molecules moving in a volume V becomes

$$Z_N = \frac{\Lambda^{-3N} q^N}{N!} \int_V \cdots \int_V d\mathbf{r}_1 \ldots d\mathbf{r}_N \, e^{-\mathscr{V}/kT}$$

on the assumption that the quantum length $\Lambda \; (= \sqrt{h^2/2\pi mkT})$ is small compared with the characteristic distances which specify ϕ. $\mathscr{V}$ should also include the sum $\sum_i w(\mathbf{r}_i)$ which gives the potential energy of interaction of the system with the walls of its container but this only gives rise to surface energy terms in the thermodynamic potentials, so we neglect it for the moment and take the effect of the walls to be simply to restrain every position $\mathbf{r}_i$ within V. If the molecules do not interact, the multiple integral is just V^N, and the expression reproduces the partition function for an ideal gas with q the partition function for the rotation and internal motion of one molecule.

A typical shape for ϕ is shown in Fig. 5. An effective diameter for the molecule is defined by d. This is obviously dependent on T, but the variation will be slight if ϕ rises sufficiently steeply near $r = d$. Surrounding each molecular centre, then, is a volume $b_0 = 4\pi d^3/3$ which is seldom penetrated by the centres of other molecules. At any instant, then, any one molecule is effectively excluded from a volume $(N-1)b_0$ out of the total V (and from a relatively negligible volume of the order of $V^{2/3}d$ spread over the walls).

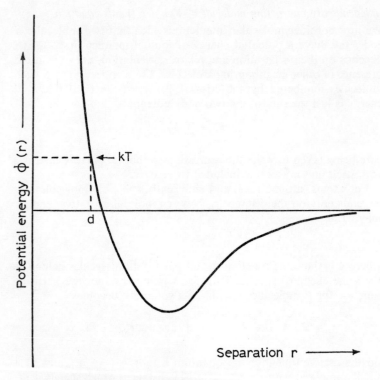

Fig. 5 Potential energy of interaction of two molecules as a function of the separation of their centres.

Having thus eliminated the configurations in which the molecular interaction energies would be very large, we seek an estimate of the effect of attraction. The sum $\mathscr{V}$ is in fact half the sum over *all* molecules of each molecule's interaction with all its fellows, so it is $N/2$ times the average potential energy of interaction of one molecule with the rest. This average is taken over molecules for *one* configuration of the whole system. We now require the average of $\exp(-\beta\mathscr{V})$ over all configurations, and estimate this by taking instead $\exp[-\beta(\text{average of } \mathscr{V})]$.

This step appears not to be valid unless the fluctuations of $\mathscr{V}$ are small compared with kT. The last condition can only be met if the attractive part of ϕ is very small, and if that is so, the attractive interaction can only be important if it has a long range to compensate.

This estimate is quantitatively good only for an unrealistic type of interaction, but leads to some reasonable deductions. The average value of $\mathscr{V}$ is now $N/2$ times the average interaction of one molecule with the others, which is itself proportional to the density of these others, and this we take as N/V. Thus the average $\mathscr{V}$ is $-N^2A/2V$ and the partition function

$$Z_N = (N!)^{-1}\Lambda^{-3N}q^N(V-Nb_0)^N \, e^{N^2A/2VkT}$$

The corresponding Helmholtz free energy F is then

$$F = -kT \ln Z_N$$
$$= F_{\text{ideal}}(N, V-Nb_0) - N^2A/2V$$

and

$$p = -\frac{\partial F}{\partial V}$$
$$= \frac{NkT}{V-Nb_0} - \frac{N^2A}{2V^2}$$

i.e.

$$\left(p+\frac{N^2A}{2V^2}\right)(V-Nb_0) = NkT$$

which is the well-known equation of state of Van der Waals.

At high temperatures, the presence of one molecule will hardly affect the density in its neighbourhood, so A should be given by

$$-\int_d^\infty 4\pi r^2\phi(r)\,\mathrm{d}r$$

At lower temperatures, molecules will tend to linger in each other's attractive field, and A will increase as

$$-\int_d^\infty 4\pi r^2\phi(r)\,e^{-\phi(r)/kT}\,\mathrm{d}r$$

This increase describes quite well the variation of the second virial coefficient of a number of gases with temperature. In view of the loose averaging procedure discussed above, one should not expect the expression to give a good absolute value.

The virial expansion

We now outline a method which is rigorous in principle, but impossibly laborious in practice, for deriving the equation of state in the form of the virial expansion, that is, expressing pV as a power series in V^{-1}. If the grand partition function were expanded in such a series, the virial expansion would be had by taking the logarithm and eliminating μ. The power series which represents the logarithm of a given power series is known, though the expression of its general term is unpleasantly complicated.

We start with the familiar expression for the canonical partition function for a classical system of independently interacting identical molecules, suppressing, for simplicity, the factors referring to rotation and internal motion of the molecules. The expression is directly valid for a system of rare gas atoms.

$$Z(N, V, T) = \frac{\Lambda^{-3N}}{N!} \int \ldots \int d\mathbf{r}_1 \ldots d\mathbf{r}_N \, e^{-\mathscr{V}/kT}$$

where

$$\mathscr{V} = \sum_{i>j} \phi(r_{ij}), \quad r_{ij} = |\mathbf{r}_j - \mathbf{r}_i|$$

The exponential is thus a product of factors $\exp(-\phi_{ij}/kT)$, each containing the positions of only two molecules and different from unity only when these molecules are fairly close together. This property suggests an ingenious substitution due to Mayer

$$e^{-\phi_{ij}/kT} = 1 + f_{ij}$$

Then

$$e^{-\mathscr{V}/kT} = 1 + \sum_{i>j} f_{ij} + \sum\sum f_{ij}f_{kl} + \cdots$$

Restrictions on the subscripts, which become complicated to write down for later terms, have to express the requirements that each interaction, of molecule i with molecule j, say, may be named at most once in any term, and that a particular term must not be counted more than once. A particular molecule, i, say, may be named as taking part in several interactions in one term.

Each factor f_{ij} is only significant when r_{ij} is within the effective range of molecular force. Thus for the simple term which consists of one f_{ij} alone, integration over all $\mathbf{r}_i$ and $\mathbf{r}_j$ within V gives a factor of V arising from the free range of $\mathbf{r}_i$, with $\mathbf{r}_j - \mathbf{r}_i$ fixed, while variation of $\mathbf{r}_j - \mathbf{r}_i$ makes a constant contribution independent of V.

The unit first term of the expansion, then, gives V^N on integration, while the $\frac{1}{2}N(N-1)$ terms containing one interaction each give V^{N-1} times a constant. In a general term, the appearance of common subscripts in factors such as f_{ij}, f_{ik} implies a linking of molecules in such a way that the term is only significant when all members of a 'cluster' are near each other. If a term referring to n molecules contains m clusters, it yields on integration V^{N+m-n} multiplied by constant factors, and m cannot be more than $\frac{1}{2}n$. For example, for three molecules, $m = 1$, and for four molecules, $m = 1$ or 2, while for four molecules in one cluster the number of interactions may range from three to six.

The contribution to Z arising from a particular term depends on the number and size of the clusters, and the pattern of their internal connections, but not on the particular molecules named. Thus many terms give the same contribution on integration. The numbers and sizes of clusters are constrained to constitute a partition of N.

Since the evaluation of Z involves a sum over partitions of N, there is good reason to evade this problem, as usual, by proceeding at once to the grand partition function

$$\Xi = \sum_N e^{\mu N/kT} Z(N, V, T)$$

The further development is elegant but elaborate.[1] However we can without difficulty find the first terms in Z, obtaining

$$Z(N, V, T) = \frac{1}{N!} \left(\frac{V}{\Lambda^3}\right)^N + \frac{1}{(N-2)!} \left(\frac{V}{\Lambda^3}\right)^{N-2} \frac{V}{\Lambda^6}$$
$$\times \frac{1}{2} \int [e^{-\phi_{12}/kT} - 1]\, d\mathbf{r}_{12} \dots$$

$$= \frac{1}{N!} \left(\frac{V}{\Lambda^3}\right)^N + \frac{1}{(N-2)!} \left(\frac{V}{\Lambda^3}\right)^{N-1} \frac{2\pi}{\Lambda^3} \int [e^{-\phi(r)/kT} - 1]$$
$$\times r^2\, dr \dots$$

$$= Z_{\text{ideal}}(N, V, T) \left[1 + \frac{N(N-1)}{V} 2\pi \int_0^\infty [e^{-\phi(r)/kT} - 1] \right.$$
$$\left. \times r^2\, dr \dots \right]$$

The series in the brackets has the extremely alarming property that the size of its second term depends not only on N/V but on N as well. Thus for a constant physical condition defined by T and N/V, we may reverse the balance of the series by increasing the size of the system considered.

Caution can be overdone. If the expansion in V^{-1} converges at

[1] We refer to the treatments in Hill's *Statistical mechanics* (see Further Reading, p. 146) and in *Theory of linear graphs* by Uhlenbeck and Ford (*Studies in statistical mechanics*, vol. 1, Ed. de Boer and Uhlenbeck, North Holland Publishing Co., 1962).

all, we have the correct first terms, and for V, as it must be, much larger than

$$v \equiv \int_0^\infty [e^{-\phi/kT} - 1] r^2 \, dr$$

we may choose N to make the second term small so that

$$F = F_{\text{ideal}} - kT \frac{N(N-1)}{V} 2\pi v \dots$$

and

$$\frac{p}{kT} = \frac{N}{V} - \left(\frac{N}{V}\right)^2 2\pi v \dots$$

which is physically sensible. The question whether the series are well-behaved lies well beyond our present scope. The result for this virial coefficient is in fact exact.

Problem: For what condition on ϕ would the second virial coefficient derived here coincide with that obtained from the van der Waals equation derived above?

Physical clusters

For some purposes it is important to estimate the very small concentration of relatively large molecular clusters present in a gas in equilibrium. When a saturated vapour is suddenly cooled, for example by adiabatic expansion, detectable droplets are most readily formed by the growth of the largest clusters previously present. Although in a natural atmosphere such clusters are generally stabilized by the presence of solutes such as salt, it is interesting to estimate what would happen in a pure substance. To do this, we extend the treatment of dissociation given above.

Suppose that at any moment the vapour of a pure substance in a given volume V can be regarded as made up of single molecules and clusters of two, three and more. Let there be N_j clusters containing the same number j of molecules, and let the partition function for the rotation and internal motion of such a cluster be q_j. The canonical partition function for N molecules is then

$$Z(N, V, T) = \sum_{\text{partitions}} \prod_j \frac{1}{N_j!} \left(\frac{Vq_j}{\Lambda_j^3}\right)^{N_j}$$

where the sum runs over all partitions of N into groups of various j so that $\sum_j jN_j = N$.

The sorting out of this sum is not straightforward, so we simplify the calculation by specifying the chemical potential μ instead of N. Now

$$\Xi(\mu, V, T) = \sum_N Z(N, V, T)\, e^{\mu N/kT}$$

$$= \sum_N \sum_{\text{partitions}} \prod_j \frac{1}{N_j!} \left(\frac{Vq_j\, e^{j\mu/kT}}{\Lambda_j^3} \right)^{N_j}$$

Since any arbitrarily selected set of N_j now gives an admissible member of the sum, we have no partition problem and can write

$$\Xi = \prod_j \sum_{N_j=0}^{\infty} \frac{1}{N_j!} \left(\frac{Vq_j\, e^{j\mu/kT}}{\Lambda_j^3} \right)^{N_j}$$

$$= \exp\left[\sum_j (Vq_j\Lambda_j^{-3}\, e^{j\mu/kT}) \right]$$

$$\equiv \exp\left(pV/kT \right)$$

so

$$\frac{p}{kT} = \sum_{j=1}^{\infty} q_j\Lambda_j^{-3}\, e^{j\mu/kT}$$

The expectation number of clusters with j members is the sum of each possible value of N_j times the relative weight of those terms which correspond to this N_j. This is

$$\overline{N_j} = q_j \frac{\partial \ln \Xi}{\partial q_j} = \frac{Vq_j}{\Lambda_j^3}\, e^{j\mu/kT}$$

each set of clusters contributing to the pressure, then, as an ideal gas of N_j molecules.

For $j=1$ this is restating our neglect of passing interactions between molecules, for the equation relates $\overline{N_1}$ to μ for an ideal monomolecular gas.

Further progress depends on taking a specific form for the q_j. It is reasonable that a large cluster in the vapour should have the structure of whichever condensed phase equilibrates with vapour at the specified temperature. Let the chemical potential in that phase be μ_c at the given temperature and pressure p. Then the Gibbs free energy of a group of j molecules in the interior of the condensed phase is $j\mu_c$, and the corresponding Helmholtz free energy is $j\mu_c - pv_j$ where v_j is the volume of the group. The free energy of the cluster is greater than this by its surface free energy, which we write as $S_j\sigma_j$: S_j may be defined to be $4\pi r_j^2$ where $v_j = 4\pi r_j^3/3$; σ_j is likely to vary substantially with j for small j.

Problem: Disregarding all thermal motions, estimate σ_j for small values of j for a substance with nearest-neighbour bonds only and a face-centred cubic crystal structure. Count broken bonds and be careful about factors of 2.

The expectation $\overline{N}_j$ may now be expressed as

$$N_j = \frac{V}{\Lambda_j^3} \exp\left[\frac{j(\mu-\mu_c)+pv_j-S_j\sigma_j}{kT}\right] \mathscr{R}_j$$

or since $\Lambda_j = j^{-1/2}\Lambda_1$,

$$\frac{\overline{N}_j}{\overline{N}_1} = \frac{j^{3/2}}{q_1} \exp\left[\frac{-\mu}{kT}\right] \exp\left[\frac{j(\mu-\mu_c)+pv_j-S_j\sigma_j}{kT}\right] \frac{\mathscr{R}_j}{\mathscr{R}_1}$$

In these expressions, the factor $\mathscr{R}_j$ is introduced to allow for the free rotation of the cluster in the vapour, compared with the restrictions on its rotation when buried in the condensed phase. This factor will be greatest when the condensed phase is solid, since three degrees of freedom which are then transverse waves, with wavelength of the order of twice the diameter of the cluster, become degrees of free rotation when the cluster is released into the vapour.

The transverse wave of wavelength $4r_j$ has frequency $c/4r_j$, where c is the appropriate speed of sound, and the corresponding partition function at high enough temperature is $(4r_j kT/c)^3$ for three degrees of freedom.

An accurate estimate of the rotational partition function is beyond the scope of this book (see, for example, Rushbrooke), but its order of magnitude is well enough given if we take the p.f. for a linear molecule, which has two rotational degrees of freedom, and raise it to the three-halves power, $(2IkT/\hbar^2)^{3/2}$. This gives then

$$\mathscr{R}_j = \frac{\pi}{6v_j}\left(\frac{Ic^2}{2\hbar^2kT}\right)^{3/2}$$

A fair guess for a liquid may be made if we imagine a hypodermic syringe with a needle of molecular dimensions immersed in the bulk liquid. Liquid may be drawn in reversibly with zero expenditure of work, provided the liquid just wets the wall of the syringe, and we suppose a drop of molecules extruded into the vapour region by doing an amount of work determined by the pressure change and the surface energy.

While the drop remains attached by a small part of its surface to the needle of the syringe, those modes of motion which will become the free rotations correspond to oscillations controlled by the surface tension of the drop, with frequency σ_j/m_j where σ_j is the surface tension and m_j the drop mass. The partition function is $(kTm_j/h\sigma_j)^3$ and correspondingly

$$\mathscr{R}_j = \left(\frac{2\pi\sigma_j}{m_j}\right)^3\left(\frac{2I}{kT}\right)^{3/2}$$

Problem: Estimate $\mathscr{R}_j$ for ice and water clusters with $j=10$ and 100, at 0°C.

Although $\mathscr{R}_j$ is not negligible, its interpretation is still doubtful. After all, one could have defined $\mathscr{R}_j$ to be unity, and subsumed the rotation effects into the variation of σ_j. In any event, $\mathscr{R}_j$ varies as a low power of T, and the exponential will dominate it completely. We neglect it in the next paragraphs.

The condition of equilibrium between condensed phase and vapour is $\mu=\mu_c$. The vapour can of course exist by itself at $\mu<\mu_c$. States of the vapour for which $\mu>\mu_c$ represent supersaturation and are at most metastable. However, in supersaturated vapour, small clusters are still more likely to evaporate than to grow.

The Gibbs free energy of a cluster is $j\mu_c+S_j\sigma_j$ so the chemical potential in it is $\mu_c+(S_{j+1}\sigma_{j+1}-S_j\sigma_j)$. If $\sigma_{j+1}=\sigma_j$, the chemical potential is

$$\mu_c+ \sigma \frac{\mathrm{d}S}{\mathrm{d}j} = \mu_c+\frac{2\sigma v}{r}$$

where v is the molecular volume in the condensed phase.

For any μ larger than μ_c, then, there exists an r such that $\mu=\mu_c+2\sigma v/r$, giving the radius of the cluster which is by itself in equilibrium at this μ. Smaller clusters are more likely to evaporate than grow; larger ones are more likely to grow beyond limit (i.e. in practice, till they fall out of the supersaturated vapour region).

In a supersaturated vapour it is strictly nonsense to discuss thermodynamic equilibrium conditions, but a kinetic discussion, which lies outside our present scope, shows that at low supersaturations the concept of a definite μ is valid and the 'equilibrium' expression for $\overline{N_j}/\overline{N_1}$ remains reasonable so long as j is well below its value, $(\pi/6v) \times [2\sigma v/(\mu-\mu_c)]^3$, for the equilibrium cluster.

It is important to note that even if the problems of evaluating $\mathscr{R}_j$ and of defining σ_j were resolved, we have not constructed a correct account of the imperfect gas. The reason lies in the difficulty of making a clear distinction between a cluster and a momentarily close group of molecules. If a distinction is imposed in dynamical terms, the cluster needs to have a bounded energy (negative, for the usual choice of energy zero). This is incompatible with a well-defined temperature, so q_j must be redefined. This can of course be done, but one loses the simplicity which makes the approximate model instructive.

A very simply related discussion can be applied to find the equilibrium density of bubbles in a liquid. Here again, a bubble in a superheated liquid must pass a certain size before it reaches the 'runaway' state of continuing growth. The absence of suitable nuclei is responsible for the phenomenon of 'bumping' in the boiling of clean liquids. Two familiar devices for detecting the tracks of high energy particles, the Wilson cloud chamber and the Glaser bubble chamber, depend on the nucleation of an unstable fluid. In the cloud chamber, drops are nucleated by ions, which stabilize the condensed phase with its high dielectric constant: in the bubble chamber, the bubbles are nucleated by intense local heating associated with the short tracks of slow electrons.

7

ORDERING ON A LATTICE

The lattice gas

Solute molecules in a crystal lattice or adsorbed molecules on a crystal surface, if they are sufficiently tightly bound that each molecule vibrates many times about one position of mechanical equilibrium before making a diffusive jump to another similar position, give rise to a simplified statistical problem in that the integral over all configurations reduces to a sum over a finite set of crystal arrangements.

Mutual exclusion effects appear naturally in the condition that only one molecule may occupy one site (or connected group of neighbouring sites) at one time. The simplest situation arises when one molecule occupies one site and interacts only, and independently, with its nearest neighbours. As was seen in the previous chapter, this is a case of the Ising problem. For a structure in more than one dimension, an approximate method of solution must be employed.

Consider a crystalline structure of N molecular sites. Each site is surrounded by z equidistant nearest neighbours, which may or may not be nearest neighbours to each other according to the particular structure type. In the body-centred cubic lattice, z is 8 and no nearest neighbour of a given molecule is nearest neighbour to another member of the group: in the face-centred cubic lattice, z is 12 and each nearest neighbour of a given molecule is nearest neighbour to four other members of the group.

The total number of 'bonds' joining nearest neighbours in this structure is $\frac{1}{2}zN$, for each molecule is the terminus of z bonds and each bond has two terminal molecules. To fix our ideas, consider a solid solution of N_A molecules of species A with N_B molecules of species B, where $N_A + N_B = N$. These molecules can be arranged in a vast number of configurations in which the numbers of AA, AB and BB nearest neighbour bonds vary widely.

For example, if all the A molecules are aggregated into a crystal region of pure A, the number of AA bonds (disregarding the surface of the A region) is $\frac{1}{2}zN_A$. If on the other hand N_A is small enough ($\leqslant N_B$, for the body-centred cubic structure), the A atoms may be dispersed so that the number n_{AA} of AA bonds is zero. Since in general the energy of an AA bond differs from that of an AB, and in turn from that of a BB bond, different values of n_{AA} correspond to different energies of the crystal even for constant N_A.

Since each AA bond involves two A atoms, its formation entails the loss of two potential AB bonds, so the number of AB bonds is necessarily $zN_A - 2n_{AA}$. The number of BB bonds must then evidently be $\frac{1}{2}zN - zN_A + n_{AA}$. Thus the numbers of AA, AB and BB bonds are determined when N, N_A and any one of n_{AA}, n_{AB} or n_{BB} are known.

As a rule, different configurations will give rise to different normal modes of vibration for the structure, but the mechanical problem of determining these modes is very intractable. The simplest procedure will be to adopt an Einstein model, in which each molecule is supposed to vibrate independently in the average potential field determined by its neighbours (we ignore anharmonic effects in the potential field arising from its neighbours at rest in their equilibrium positions). This will be considered independently of the configuration problem (see pp. 105–106).

The potential energy of the system at rest, and a reasonable approximation to the molecular oscillations, will be determined by the numbers of bonds present of the three distinct types, and so by N, N_A, n_{AA} in particular. We therefore require to know the number of distinct configurations of the system, given these three numbers. This has been directly obtained for the one-dimensional problem, but is not so easily estimated for two and three dimensions.

It is clear that if n_{AA} is not specified, the number of distinct arrangements of N_A, A molecules and N_B, B molecules is $N!/(N_A!)(N_B!)$ for a given set of N sites.[1] This result, while not immediately helpful, provides a useful constraint on any approximation.

---

[1] Students may rightly worry about the fact that the N sites are determined by the interaction of the molecules and not magically provided in advance. A cluster of N connected sites of a given crystal structure may take an enormous variety of shapes and attitudes, but those which deviate far from a convex shape, which is (roughly) the shape of minimum surface area (and, exactly, the

Another helpful preliminary result comes from considering a wholly random distribution of molecules, such as may arise if A and B differ only by an isotopic substitution. The expectation number of A neighbours of a given site is then zN_A/N, and the expectation number of B neighbours is zN_B/N. The expectation numbers of AA and BB bonds are therefore $\frac{1}{2}zN_A^2/N$ and $\frac{1}{2}zN_B^2/N$ respectively, and the expectation number of AB bonds is zN_AN_B/N. We have then for the random arrangement

$$n_{AB}^2 = 4n_{AA}n_{BB}$$

Quasi-chemical approximation

The above result agrees, for zero value of the ordering energy, with the quasi-chemical equation, exact in one dimension,

$$\frac{n_{AB}^2}{n_{AA}n_{BB}} = 4e^{-2E/kT}$$

with $E = E_{AB} - \frac{1}{2}(E_{AA} + E_{BB})$ where $E_{\alpha\beta}$ is the energy (*not* the binding energy, but the negative of a binding energy) of an $\alpha\beta$ bond.[1]

Rearrangement of the equation in terms of n ($\equiv n_{AA}$) alone gives the quadratic

$$z^2N_A^2 - 2zN\,e^{-x}\,n - 4zN_A(1 - e^{-x})n + 4(1 - e^{-x})n^2 = 0$$

where $x = 2E/kT$. The balance of power in the middle of the equation depends essentially on the relative value of N_A/N and $\exp(-x)$. Very large x leads to $n = zN_A/2$, the condition of complete segregation of the A molecules in a single cluster, while zero x gives the value of n corresponding to the completely random distribution.

The solution of the quadratic is conveniently expressed in terms of a variable $y \equiv e^x - 1$, and we obtain

$$n = \frac{zN_A}{2} + \frac{zN}{4y} \pm \frac{zN}{4y} \sqrt{(1 + 4yN_AN_B/N^2)}$$

---

shape of minimum surface free energy), have high surface free energy and correspondingly low probability of occurrence in thermodynamic equilibrium. So long as we only wish to discuss bulk properties, then, variations of shape of the group of N sites may be neglected.

[1] Guggenheim was the first to suggest that the quasi-chemical equation could be assumed to hold generally. He derived various consequences, and, with others, later showed that this quasi-chemical approximation is exactly equivalent to that form of Bethe's approximation in which the Bethe sub-system consists of one site with all of its nearest neighbours. We have already obtained the quasi-chemical equation by the Bethe method for the one-dimensional system, and a further discussion of the quasi-chemical method is given in a later section. (The proof of the general equivalence is to be found in more elaborate texts.)

Since the maximum geometrically possible value of n is $zN_A/2$, and the minimum is zero, it is evident that only the negative root gives an acceptable solution. The effective tendency to aggregate is seen to depend on the value of $4yN_AN_B/N^2$. Provided this is numerically small it is a suitable variable in which to expand the square root, and the solution to second order in y is then

$$n = \frac{zN_A^2}{2N}(1 + yN_B^2N^{-2} - 2y^2N_AN_B^3N^{-4}\ldots)$$

For small N_A, $N_B \doteqdot N$ and we have nearly

$$n = \frac{zN_A^2}{2N}e^{2E/kT}$$

In the true lattice gas situation $2E = -E_{AA}$, which is the binding energy between two neighbouring molecules.

Thus in the dilute gas the concentration of 'dimers' differs from its value for a purely random distribution only by the factor exp (binding energy/kT), provided $|y| \ll N/4N_A$. This corresponds in form to the result for the concentration of dimers in a dissociating gas, which was obtained above on the assumption of saturating forces.

The similarity of these estimates is not surprising, for, if the concentration of monomer is so low that no aggregates larger than dimers are likely to be present, the difference between saturating and independent interactions has no chance to manifest itself. If we go back to the exact solution of the quadratic, however, we have a result, limited only by the correctness of the quasi-chemical approximation, which may be written

$$n = \frac{zN_A}{2} + \frac{zN}{4y}[1 - \sqrt{1+k'y}]$$

The internal energy of the lattice gas is then

$$U = nE_{AA}$$

and the entropy

$$S = \int_0^T T^{-1}\frac{\partial U}{\partial T}\,\partial T$$

The integration, though laborious, is elementary, provided $y > 0$, and leads to the Helmholtz free energy

$$F = \tfrac{1}{2}zN_AE_{AA} + NkT[\theta\ln\theta + (1-\theta)\ln(1-\theta)]$$

$$+ \tfrac{1}{2}zNkT\left[\theta\ln\frac{\beta-1+2\theta}{\theta(\beta+1)} + (1-\theta)\ln\frac{\beta+1-2\theta}{(1-\theta)(\beta+1)}\right]$$

where $\theta = N_A/N$, $\beta = (1 + k'y)^{1/2}$, $y = \exp(-E_{AA}/kT) - 1$. Note that all but the first term of this expression is symmetric between θ and $(1 - \theta)$.

Problem: Evaluate $(\partial F/\partial N)_{N_A}$ and deduce an effective pressure for the lattice gas with attractive interaction.

In the true lattice gas, E is half the binding energy of an AA pair and is generally positive. In a solid solution, however, E may take either sign, so we must consider also negative values of y. Since y now goes to -1 as T goes to zero, the integral leading to F no longer converges, indicating that this form of quasi-chemical approximation must be breaking down at $T = 0$. One reason is in fact quite evident. If we ignore surface bonds, the requirement $n_{AB} = 0$, which arises from $T = 0$, $E > 0$, can always be fulfilled by complete segregation. On the other hand, the requirement n_{AA} or $n_{BB} = 0$, arising from $T = 0$, $E < 0$, is geometrically possible only for special structures and concentrations. For example, in a face-centred cubic lattice with $N_A = N/4$, all A atoms may be set on one of the four simple cubic lattices which interlace in this structure, to give $n_{AA} = 0$, but $n_{AA} > 0$ for any $N_A/N > \frac{1}{4}$.

Systems of this sort, in which an ordered state exists for suitable concentrations and low enough temperatures, are of particular interest. The configurational entropy associated with the distribution of molecules over lattice positions is best estimated by reference to the ideally ordered state. This calculation will be discussed in a later section (pp. 108–117).

Molecular oscillations in the lattice gas

The vibration of a molecule about its equilibrium position in the lattice will depend on its own nature and on the nature and relative disposition of its neighbours. For example, an A with two A neighbours will behave differently according to whether these are polar opposites or lie next to each other. As a crude estimate, however, we might neglect this and set each molecule in a spherically symmetric oscillator potential whose stiffness depended only on the number of neighbours of each type.

Then the vibration rate ω_{Aa} for an A molecule with a, A neighbours would be given by

$$\omega_{Aa}^2 = \frac{1}{z}[a\omega_{Az}^2 + (z - a)\omega_{A0}^2]$$

In a binary solid solution, we should have correspondingly

$$\omega_{Ba}^2 = \frac{1}{z}[a\omega_{Bz}^2 + (z-a)\omega_{B0}^2]$$

where $m_B\omega_{Bz}^2 = m_A\omega_{A0}^2$ if the AB bonds for B surrounded by A and A surrounded by B have in fact the same stiffness. Moreover, it would not be surprising if ω_{Az}^2/E_{AA} were nearly equal to ω_{A0}^2/E_{AB}.

At sufficiently low concentration we need consider only $a=0$ and 1, having $N_A - 2n_{AA}$ isolated molecules and $2n_{AA}$ molecules with one A nearest neighbour. At temperatures high enough for the Einstein approximation to be worth using, the partition function for each degree of freedom with angular frequency ω is just $kT/\hbar\omega$.

Even within the approximation of associating a fixed spring constant with each type of bond, it would be more realistic to distinguish the different normal modes of the AA pair, but it is rather doubtfully worth while. This sort of analysis is certainly needed when one studies lattice mechanics, for example by neutron diffraction, but other unrealities of the model are probably more important when comparison is made only with thermodynamic data.

Problem: Find the free energy of a dilute lattice gas of N_A, A molecules on N sites, using the above assumption about their oscillations and assuming (falsely) that A and AA molecules are independently distributed over the lattice. Note that the centres of AA molecules have $\frac{1}{2}zN$ possible sites.

Order and disorder

It is well known that a number of metallic alloys, whose compositions are close to simple atomic proportions such as AB or AB_3, have an orderly structure at low temperatures, quite analogous to the structure of ionic crystals with similar atomic ratios. These ordered alloys are frequently rather brittle and resonant. They pass at higher temperatures into a disordered state in which the general lattice structure is unchanged but atoms of different species do not concentrate on distinct sets of lattice points. The order–disorder transition is generally accompanied by a large peak in the specific heat–temperature graph, but a small or apparently zero latent heat at the precise transition temperature. The typical variation is as shown, the transition being called a λ-point by an obvious similarity.

We have already met a difficulty in applying the quasi-chemical equation to the Ising lattice gas when the interaction is such that like atoms or molecules have an energetic preference for remaining apart. This is, however, the situation that corresponds to order in such

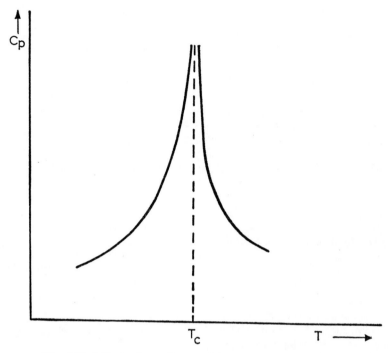

Fig. 6 Variation of specific heat with temperature round a typical λ-point transition.

alloys as FeAl, in which two simple cubic lattices of aluminium and iron atoms interpenetrate in such a way that each cube of iron has an aluminium atom at its centre and vice versa. In the state of ideal order at the exact stoichiometric composition, all nearest-neighbour bonds in this structure are of AB type. It will be interesting to see how far approximate methods can deal with the ordering at finite temperature and possibly non-stoichiometric composition.

The geometrical impossibility of fitting the previous quasi-chemical equation for some temperatures and compositions suggests that the lower[1] symmetry of the ordered state ought to be recognized from the beginning in setting up the theory.

---

[1] The association of lower symmetry with ordering is due to the fact that a highly structured situation has fewer symmetry elements than, for example, an isotropic situation. Thus a gas or liquid (far from any rigid boundary) has complete spatial symmetry; a crystal has less, and an ordered crystal less again.

This is not very satisfactory, for a good theory ought to derive the breach of symmetry from the molecular interactions. In the present state of knowledge, progress in this direction depends on rather advanced theoretical technique. A more empirical approach, accepting the experimental knowledge, which we already have, as prescribing the expected order for an alloy of given type, is very much easier.

In a given ordering system, then, we consider the structure of its highly ordered condition as determined, say, by diffraction experiments. The whole lattice is divided into the sub-lattices occupied by atoms of different species in the ordered state, and various order parameters are defined to describe the partial order which is all that we ever actually have.

These order parameters fall into two groups. One set actually vanishes above the transition point, when the populations of the different sub-lattices contain identical fractions of the various species: they determine the long-range order. The others relate to the deviation of the numbers of the various bond types from their values for a perfectly random atomic distribution, and vanish only at infinite temperature: they describe the short-range order.

In the simplest situation, one long-range and one short-range parameter suffice. We consider as an example of this an alloy of composition $A_x B_y$, with the A and B atoms occupying N sites of a body-centred cubic lattice.

There are then N_A atoms of the type A and N_B of type B, where $N_A/N_B = x/y$ and $N_A + N_B = N$. FeAl is an alloy of this class. The lattice consists of two simple cubic sub-lattices, and every atom in either sub-lattice is at the centre of a cubic cell of the other sub-lattice: its nearest neighbours are the eight atoms at the corners of that cube. When $x = y$, the state of perfect order is that described above, with all the A atoms on one sub-lattice, all the B atoms on the other, and all bonds in the structure of AB type.

One sub-lattice is called the α lattice, the other β, and we decide arbitrarily to call an A atom rightly situated if it is on the α lattice, wrongly situated if it is on the β lattice. Of the N_A, A atoms, R_A lie on α and $N_A - R_A$ on β: of the N_B, B atoms, R_B lie on β and $N_B - R_B$ on α. The number of wrongly occupied α sites is $W_A = N_B - R_B = \frac{1}{2}N - R_A$, and is the number of wrongly placed B atoms. The number of wrongly occupied β sites is $W_B = N_A - R_A = \frac{1}{2}N - R_B$. If a portion of the alloy is in the ordered state, the sensible choice of the α lattice will be that sub-lattice with most A atoms on it, otherwise the choice is insignificant. The choice of long-range order parameter is to some extent also arbitrary. It is reasonable to choose it to vanish when the sets of A and B atoms are both evenly divided between the α and β lattices. A possible choice is

$$\mathscr{S} = 2(2R_A - N_A)/N = 2(2R_B - N_B)/N$$

which vanishes, as desired, when $R_A = \frac{1}{2}N_A$. The factor $2/N$ gives the second convenient property that $\mathscr{S} = 1$ for $R_A = N_A = N/2$—perfect ordering of the 50–50 alloy. We have then

$$R_A = \tfrac{1}{2}N_A + \tfrac{1}{4}\mathscr{S}N, \qquad R_B = \tfrac{1}{2}N_B + \tfrac{1}{4}\mathscr{S}N$$
$$W_A = \tfrac{1}{2}N - R_A = \tfrac{1}{2}N_B - \tfrac{1}{4}\mathscr{S}N$$
$$W_B = \tfrac{1}{2}N_A - \tfrac{1}{4}\mathscr{S}N$$

Neither W_A nor W_B may be negative, and if $N_A > N_B$, which we may always choose to make true by which atom we choose to call A, only W_A may be zero. The greatest value of $\mathscr{S}$ is then $2N_B/N$, which we shall call y. (Then $2N_A/N = x$, say, and $x + y = 2$.)

Let the number of nearest neighbours of one atom (actually 8 in b.c.c.) be z. Then the number of bonds in the structure is $\tfrac{1}{2}Nz$ and each bond joins one α to one β site. Since 'right' and 'wrong' atoms are distinguished in the ordered state, we distinguish between AB bonds, joining right atoms with A on α and B on β, and BA bonds, joining wrong atoms with A on β and B on α, although AB and BA bonds have identical energy. Let the numbers of bonds of the different types be Q_{AA}, Q_{AB}, Q_{BA}, Q_{BB}. These numbers are connected, as may be seen by considering in turn the bonds which end on right and wrong, A and B atoms.

Thus

$$Q_{AA} + Q_{AB} = zR_A$$
$$Q_{AA} + Q_{BA} = zW_B$$
$$Q_{BB} + Q_{BA} = zW_A$$
$$Q_{BB} + Q_{AB} = zR_B$$

or

$$Q_{AA} = zR_A - Q_{AB}$$
$$Q_{BB} = zR_B - Q_{AB}$$
$$Q_{BA} = zW_B - Q_{AA} = Q_{AB} - \tfrac{1}{2}z\mathscr{S}N$$

so once N_A, N_B and $\mathscr{S}$ are known, Q_{AB} suffices to define all the Q and so the bond energy. We shall see Q_{AB} itself as a short-range order parameter, though something more elegant can easily be manufactured.

The total bond energy is simply

$$E(Q) = Q_{AA}E_{AA} + Q_{BB}E_{BB} + (Q_{AB} + Q_{BA})E_{AB}$$
$$= \tfrac{1}{2}zN_AE_{AA} + \tfrac{1}{2}zN_BE_{BB} + (2Q_{AB} - \tfrac{1}{2}z\mathscr{S}N)A$$

where A is the Ising energy $E_{AB} - \tfrac{1}{2}(E_{AA} + E_{BB})$. This use of the letter A is consistent with the previous chapter, and should cause no confusion.

We come now to the much harder problem of estimating the number of configurations of given energy, that is, for given values of $\mathscr{S}$ and Q_{AB}. If $\mathscr{S}$ alone is fixed, the count is easy. We have to distribute R_A, A atoms over $N/2$, α sites, and independently to distribute R_B, B atoms over the β sites. The number of distinct configurations is then

$$W(\mathscr{S}) = \frac{(N/2)!}{R_A!W_A!} \cdot \frac{(N/2)!}{R_B!W_B!}$$

These configurations, however, range over all the possible values of Q_{AB}, so do not correspond to a fixed energy.[1]

The energy is of course given by the single parameter $Q_{AB} + Q_{BA}$, but we have already been led into difficulty by relying on that alone. If Q_{AB} and Q_{BA} are separately specified, $\mathscr{S}$ is determined, and we may obtain a more reliable count of configurations.

Once the Q have been fixed, the arrangement of the various bond types is still constrained by the requirement that one atomic site can be occupied by either an A or a B atom, but not by both. Consider the imagined structure generated by a random distribution of specified bonds over the $\tfrac{1}{2}Nz$ bond positions in a body-centred cubic lattice. In general one would find the atoms at many sites specified as A by some of their bonds, and as B by others. The number of realizable distributions will be a fraction of the number of random distributions of bonds, and this fraction must depend on both $\mathscr{S}$ and Q_{AB}. To identify it would be the so-far unachieved complete solution of the problem.

---

[1] A useful and important dodge is to cut off the calculation at this stage by assigning the same suitable mean value to all states of given $\mathscr{S}$. The simplest procedure is to assign to each atom on α, $2zR_B/N$, B neighbours and $2zW_B/N$, A neighbours, and conversely. The corresponding energy we denote by $E_{BW}(\mathscr{S})$ since the method was suggested by Bragg and Williams (*Proc. Roy. Soc.* **A145**, p. 699, 1934) and then the free energy

$$F(\mathscr{S}, T) = E_{BW}(\mathscr{S}) - kT \ln W(\mathscr{S})$$

may be minimized with respect to $\mathscr{S}$ to find the thermodynamic equilibrium state.

The shortcut which generates a new variety of quasi-chemical equation is to assume that the correction factor depends on $\mathscr{S}$ alone. It is plausible, from the dependence of the number of random distributions on the Q, that the correction should be more sensitive to $Q_{AB} - Q_{BA}$ than to $Q_{AB} + Q_{BA}$, but hard to go further. At least, we can now make sure that not only are the states of given $\mathscr{S}$ correctly counted, but their energy levels are correctly listed, while we hope that the number of states on each level is not too badly distorted. This should represent an advance on both previous approximations. We write, then, for the number of configurations of given $\mathscr{S}$ and Q_{AB}

$$W(\mathscr{S}, Q) = R(\mathscr{S}) \frac{(zN/2)!}{Q_{AA}! Q_{AB}! Q_{BA}! Q_{BB}!}$$

and propose to determined $R(\mathscr{S})$ from the requirement that

$$\sum_{Q_{AB}} W(\mathscr{S}, Q) = W(\mathscr{S})$$

This need only be carried through with enough precision that $\ln W$ is known down to first order in N, since terms in $N^{2/3}$, $\ln N$, and so on are not perceived in the bulk thermodynamic functions. The quadrinomial coefficient in $W(\mathscr{S}, Q)$ rises so spectacularly to its maximum permitted value that the number of terms near that maximum which make up nearly the whole of the sum is negligible compared with the N. Thus we need locate only the minimum of $\ln (Q_{AA}! Q_{AB}! Q_{BA}! Q_{BB}!)$ for the given $\mathscr{S}$ to evaluate $\ln R(\mathscr{S})$. Stirling's expansion gives then

$$\ln W(\mathscr{S}) = 2\left(\frac{N}{2} \ln \frac{N}{2} - \frac{N}{2}\right) - R_A \ln R_A + R_A$$
$$- W_A \ln W_A + W_A - R_B \ln R_B + R_B - W_B \ln W_B + W_B$$
$$= N \ln \frac{N}{2} - \sum R \ln R$$

where $\sum R \ln R$ is a contraction for

$$R_A \ln R_A + W_A \ln W_A + R_B \ln R_B + W_B \ln W_B$$

Similarly

$$\ln W(\mathscr{S}, Q) = \ln R(\mathscr{S}) + \tfrac{1}{2}Nz \ln(\tfrac{1}{2}Nz) - \tfrac{1}{2}Nz - \sum Q \ln Q + \sum Q$$
$$= \ln R(\mathscr{S}) + \tfrac{1}{2}Nz \ln(\tfrac{1}{2}Nz) - Q_{AB} \ln Q_{AB}$$
$$- (Q_{AB} - \tfrac{1}{2}z\mathscr{S}N) \ln (Q_{AB} - \tfrac{1}{2}\mathscr{S}N)$$
$$- (zR_A - Q_{AB}) \ln (zR_A - Q_{AB})$$
$$- (zR_B - Q_{AB}) \ln (zR_B - Q_{AB})$$

Setting $q = Q_{AB}$, then, we have

$$\frac{d}{dq} \ln W(\mathscr{S}, q) = -\ln q - \ln (q - \tfrac{1}{2}z\mathscr{S}N)$$
$$+ \ln (zR_A - q) + \ln (zR_B - q)$$

which must be zero for the turning value q_0, so,

$$q_0(q_0 - \tfrac{1}{2}z\mathscr{S}N) = (zR_A - q_0)(zR_B - q_0)$$

i.e.

$$q_0 = 2zR_AR_B/N$$
$$= \frac{zN}{8}(x + \mathscr{S})(y + \mathscr{S})$$

We approximate $R(\mathscr{S})$ (or redefine it, at choice) by the relation

$$\ln W(\mathscr{S}) = N \ln \frac{N}{2} - \sum R \ln R$$
$$= \ln R(\mathscr{S}) + \tfrac{1}{2}zN \ln (\tfrac{1}{2}zN) - \sum Q_0 \ln Q_0$$

the Q_0 corresponding to the turning value. Elimination of $R(\mathscr{S})$ gives then

$$\ln W(\mathscr{S}, Q) = N \ln \frac{N}{2} - \sum R \ln R + \sum Q_0 \ln Q_0 - \sum Q \ln Q$$

and the 'constrained free energy' for given N_A, N_B, $\mathscr{S}$, Q_{AB} is

$$F = E(Q) - kT \ln W(\mathscr{S}, Q)$$

The true free energy is to be estimated by averaging over all configurations, but we use essentially the same shortcut twice more, first to find a less constrained free energy for given $\mathscr{S}$, then to find what $\mathscr{S}$ gives the thermodynamic equilibrium state. The assumption is that the average value is practically coincident with the value at the minimum of F.

To find the free energy for $\mathscr{S}$, alone, prescribed, we take the relevant part of F/kT, which is ϕ, equal to $(2AQ_{AB}/kT) + \sum Q \ln Q$, and differentiate with respect to $q = Q_{AB}$; so for the turning value

$$0 = \frac{d\phi}{dq} = (2A/kT) + \ln q + \ln (q - \tfrac{1}{2}z\mathscr{S}N) - \ln (zR_A - q) - \ln (zR_B - q)$$

or

$$e^{-2A/kT}(zR_A - q)(zR_B - q) = q(q - \tfrac{1}{2}z\mathscr{S}N)$$

i.e.

$$e^{-2A/kT} Q_{AA}Q_{BB} = Q_{AB}Q_{BA}$$

Now $Q_{AB} = Q_{BA}$ if $\mathscr{S} = 0$, and the last equation is then identical with the quasi-chemical equation used above as the starting point for the discussion of the lattice gas.

Thus if, as we shall see, there is a temperature region in which $\mathscr{S} = 0$ for the ordering system, the expressions derived above for the entropy and free energy must be valid in that region. For non-zero values of $\mathscr{S}$, $Q_{AB} \neq Q_{BA}$.

The above quadratic in q is simplified by introduction of the symbol f for $[1 - \exp(2A/kT)]^{-1}$. Since A is negative in an ordering system, f ranges from 1 at $T = 0$ to infinity at T infinite, being $-kT/2A$ for $kT \gg A$.

The solutions of the quadratic are given by

$$p \equiv \frac{4q}{zN} = f + \mathscr{S} \pm [f^2 - f(\mathscr{S}^2 + xy) + \mathscr{S}^2]^{1/2}$$

but the lower bound on f, while $q \leqslant \frac{1}{2}z\mathscr{S}N$, forbids the positive root. For large values of f

$$p \sim \mathscr{S} + \frac{1}{2}(\mathscr{S}^2 + xy)$$

which reduces to the value $\frac{1}{2}xy$ for a purely random distribution at $\mathscr{S} = 0$.

Inserting now the values of Q corresponding to the q just determined, we are to minimize

$$\chi = \frac{A}{kT}(2q - \frac{1}{2}z\mathscr{S}N) + \sum R \ln R - \sum q_0 \ln q_0 + \sum q \ln q$$

by varying $\mathscr{S}$. Because of the preceding operations, terms which arise from the implicit dependence of q_0 and q on $\mathscr{S}$ all cancel, and there remain in the derivative only

$$-\frac{zNA}{2kT} + \frac{N}{4}\ln\frac{R_A R_B}{W_A W_B} - \frac{\partial}{\partial\mathscr{S}}\left(\sum q_0 \ln q_0\right) + \frac{\partial}{\partial\mathscr{S}}\left(\sum q \ln q\right)$$

where the derivatives symbolized by $\partial/\partial\mathscr{S}$ are taken (after expressing each Q in terms of the corresponding Q_{AB}) as if q_0 and q were constants.

Thus

$$\frac{\partial}{\partial \mathscr{S}} \left(\sum Q \ln Q \right) = \sum (\ln Q + 1) \frac{\partial Q}{\partial \mathscr{S}}$$

$$= [\ln (Q - \tfrac{1}{2} z \mathscr{S} N) + 1](-\tfrac{1}{2} z N)$$

$$+ [\ln (z R_A - Q) + 1] \frac{zN}{4}$$

$$+ [\ln (z R_B - Q) + 1] \frac{zN}{4}$$

remembering that R_A, R_B both depend on $\mathscr{S}$. Then

$$\frac{d\chi}{d\mathscr{S}} = -\frac{zNA}{2kT} + \frac{N}{4} \ln \frac{R_A R_B}{W_A W_B}$$

$$+ \frac{zN}{4} \ln \frac{(z R_A - q)(z R_B - q)}{(z R_A - q_0)(z R_B - q_0)} - \frac{zN}{2} \ln \frac{q - \tfrac{1}{2} z \mathscr{S} N}{q_0 - \tfrac{1}{2} z \mathscr{S} N}$$

or, referring back to the equations defining q and q_0,

$$\frac{d\chi}{d\mathscr{S}} = \frac{N}{4} \ln \frac{R_A R_B}{W_A W_B} + \frac{zN}{4} \ln \frac{q(q_0 - \tfrac{1}{2} z \mathscr{S} N)}{q_0(q - \tfrac{1}{2} z \mathscr{S} N)}$$

and the turning point condition can be expressed in several ways, of which one is

$$\frac{2A}{kT} - \left(1 - \frac{1}{z}\right) \ln \frac{(x - \mathscr{S})(y - \mathscr{S})}{(x + \mathscr{S})(y + \mathscr{S})} = \ln \frac{(x + \mathscr{S} - p)(y + \mathscr{S} - p)}{(2\mathscr{S} - p)^2}$$

It is not hard to verify that $\mathscr{S} = 0$ always satisfies this equation. This is depressing at first glance, so we examine the nature of the turning point. The value of $d^2\chi/d\mathscr{S}^2$ at $\mathscr{S} = 0$ is

$$\frac{N^2}{4} \cdot \frac{N}{N_A N_B} + \frac{(zN)^2}{8q} - \frac{(zN)^2}{8q_0}$$

which changes sign at

$$\frac{zN}{4q} = \frac{zN}{4q_0} - \frac{1}{2z} \cdot \frac{N^2}{N_A N_B}$$

i.e.

$$\frac{xy}{p} = 2\left(1 - \frac{1}{z}\right)$$

At high temperatures q is very nearly q_0 and $\mathscr{S} = 0$ gives a minimum of free energy. As the temperature is reduced and q increases, at a critical temperature $\mathscr{S} = 0$ gives a neutral value, and below this temperature $\mathscr{S}=0$ gives a maximum of free energy. At this lower temperature an equilibrium state must appear at a non-zero $\mathscr{S}$ determined by the equation given above. This yields to numerical rather than literal analysis, and the variation of F with $\mathscr{S}$ at various temperatures is shown in Fig. 7. The equilibrium value of $\mathscr{S}$ goes to zero continuously as T tends to T_c. There is then no discontinuity in

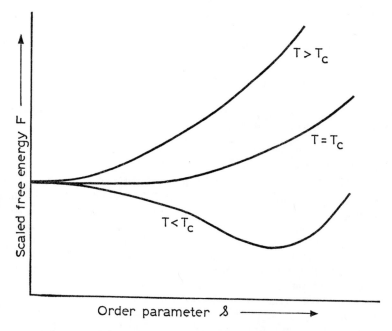

Fig. 7 Variation of free energy with long-range order at different temperatures. (The three curves are drawn on different energy scales.)

the entropy at T_c, so no latent heat, but the specific heat does increase without limit.

The critical temperature itself is now located by the equation

$$p = f - \sqrt{f^2 - fxy} = \frac{xyz}{2(z-1)}$$

For the equiatomic alloy $x=y=1$ and

$$f - \sqrt{f^2 - f} = 4/7$$

for $z = 8$. Then

$$f = 16/7 = (1 - e^{2A/kT_c})^{-1}$$

or

$$e^{2A/kT_c} = 9/16$$

i.e.

$$kT_c = -\frac{2A}{\ln(16/9)}$$

In the general case

$$f_c = \frac{xyz^2}{4(z-1)} \quad \text{and} \quad \frac{2A}{kT_c} = \ln\left(1 - \frac{4(z-1)}{xyz^2}\right)$$

giving a specific dependence of the ordering temperature on the energy A and the composition.

Comparison with experiment

The experimental determination of the ordering temperature, by diffraction measurements over a range of T which includes T_c, is in principle straightforward. A considerable practical difficulty is to ensure that the material has reached its equilibrium structure at each temperature of measurement, since the diffusive interchange of atoms is in many alloys very slow near the ordering temperature.

Another difficulty arises because at given (say, atmospheric) pressure the atomic spacing in the alloy varies with composition. The corresponding variation of the ordering energy A is not easy to evaluate. One way to estimate it would be to find the bulk modulus of elasticity of pure A, pure B, and the fully ordered AB alloy and interpret this as a variation of bond energy with bond length. This, however, is certainly unreliable if either pure substance is unobtainable with the same crystal structure as the alloy. For example, aluminium cannot be had in the body-centred cubic structure of the alloy FeAl.

A better test, then, is to conduct the experiment at various pressures so that the ordering temperature is determined as a function of composition at constant lattice spacing. This is well discussed by Yoon and Bienenstock,[1] who find that for β-brass, at least, the ordering energy is not independent of concentration even at constant atomic spacing. Their conclusion is not dependent on the approxi-

[1] D.-Y. Yoon and A. Bienenstock, *Physical Review* 170, p. 631, 1968.

mations made in our statistical argument, because correct statistics must still lead to an equation of the form

$$\frac{kT_c}{A} = f(x, z)$$

where f is determined solely by counting configurations. Thus for a set of specimens of different composition, $\partial(\ln T_c)/\partial(\ln a)$ where a is the interatomic spacing, is simply $\partial \ln A/\partial a$. Yoon and Bienenstock find that $\partial \ln T_c/\partial \ln a$ changes by 9% for a 3% change in zinc content, and observe that interactions of atoms with second-nearest as well as with nearest neighbours might readily account for this.

The introduction of simple second-neighbour interactions is not unduly hard in principle. One requires at least one new order parameter, and the statistics are most lucidly handled by explicit use of Bethe's method. The task of distinguishing whether the defeat of theoretical predictions by experimental facts is due to an unsuitable model or an inadequate calculation then becomes much harder, and the drawing of sound conclusions from experimental results correspondingly more difficult.

This basic difficulty, that the ordering phenomenon is familiar only in systems where the forces of interaction are not known in sufficient detail for a good test of the theory, recurs when we consider still more complex transitions.

8

DENSE DISORDERED SYSTEMS

Some systems without long-range order

The methods of the last chapter lead to lengthy calculations in the treatment of states of non-zero $\mathscr{S}$, below the ordering temperature. If $\mathscr{S} = 0$, on the other hand, $Q_{AB} = Q_{BA}$ and the quasi-chemical equation in its original form is valid. From the last chapter we have now, for $N\,(= N_A + N_B)$ sites carrying N_A, A and N_A, B atoms

$$Q_{AB} = Q_{BA} = \frac{zN}{4}\frac{xy}{1+\beta}$$

$$Q_{AA} = \tfrac{1}{2}zN_A - Q_{AB}$$

$$= \frac{zN}{4}\frac{x}{1+\beta}(1+\beta-y)$$

and similarly

$$Q_{BB} = \frac{zN}{4}\frac{y}{1+\beta}(1+\beta-x)$$

with

$$x = 2N_A/N, \quad y = 2N_B/N, \quad \beta^2 = 1 + xy(e^{2A/kT}-1)$$

The configuration entropy S_c can now be reduced, with a little manipulation, to the form

$$\frac{S_c}{k} = -\left[N_A \ln\left(\frac{N_A}{N}\right) + N_B \ln\left(\frac{N_B}{N}\right)\right]$$

$$+ \frac{zN}{4(1+\beta)}\left[2(1+\beta)\ln\left(\frac{1+\beta}{2}\right)\right.$$

$$\left. - x(1+\beta-y)\ln\frac{1+\beta-y}{x} - y(1+\beta-x)\ln\frac{1+\beta-x}{y}\right]$$

which shows the entropy of completely random mixing supplemented by a group of terms each of which clearly vanishes as $\beta \to 1$, that is, as $T \to \infty$, or $x \to 0$.

The bond energy is at the same time

$$U_b = \frac{zN}{4} \left(xE_{AA} + yE_{BB} + \frac{2xy}{1+\beta} A \right)$$

so the 'configuration part' of the free energy is

$$F_c = U_b - TS_c$$

which may be written as

$$\frac{zN}{4} (xE_{AA} + yE_{BB} + xyA) + kT \left[N_A \ln \left(\frac{N_A}{N} \right) + N_B \ln \left(\frac{N_B}{N} \right) \right]$$

$$-\frac{zN}{4} \left\{ \frac{\beta-1}{\beta+1} \, xyA + \frac{kT}{(1+\beta)} \left[2(1+\beta) \ln \frac{1+\beta}{2} \right. \right.$$

$$\left. \left. -x(1+\beta-y) \ln \frac{1+\beta-y}{x} - y(1+\beta-x) \ln \frac{1+\beta-x}{y} \right] \right\}$$

$$= F_{BW} + \text{correction terms}$$

where the Bragg–Williams free energy F_{BW} is obtained by setting $\beta = 1$ in F_c.

Problem: Show that if $E_{BB} = 0$ this expression is identical with that derived previously for the lattice gas. (The terms containing the factor xy cancel.)

Free energy of vibration

The above expression takes no account of molecular motion, whose contribution to the partition function may be estimated using the Einstein model discussed on p. 105 above. This gives relations of the form

$$\omega^2(\text{A on } \alpha) = \frac{1}{z} \left[\frac{Q_{AA}}{R_A} \omega_{Az}^2 + \left(z - \frac{Q_{AA}}{R_A} \right) \omega_{A0}^2 \right]$$

if we add the simplifying assumption that each atom in a site specified as, for example, A on α, vibrates as if it had the average number of A and B neighbours for all such sites.

Since the values of ω^2 given in this way depend on both order parameters, the only consistent procedure is to go right back through the calculation of the last chapter, emerging with a quasi-chemical equation and its consequences.

Problem (for the courageous): Try to construct a suitably modified quasi-chemical equation.

However, the simplifying assumption used to obtain the above value of ω^2 (A on α) is the dynamical parallel of assuming that the bond energy is to be calculated as if each atom were surrounded by the expectation set of nearest neighbours—the exact assumption of the Bragg–Williams method.

Even adding the free energy of motion, estimated from our simple assumptions, to the Bragg–Williams form of the configurational free energy is less straightforward than one might wish, except in the limit of low concentration, when an artificially small frequency shift enables us to use

$$\ln \frac{kT}{\hbar(\omega + \delta)} = -\frac{\delta}{\omega} \ln \frac{kT}{\hbar\omega}$$

Problem: (a) Find the free energy of a solid solution with $\mathscr{S} = 0$, for this simplified case. (b) Find the part of ΔF_c, given above, which is proportional to x^2 in the limit of small x, and compare it with the vibration term.

Segregation in completely disordered systems

We consider first of all a lattice gas in which the effects of thermal motion are assumed negligible compared with configuration effects, so that the concentration-dependent part of the free energy is approximately

$$F_{\text{BW}} = \theta N E_A + \frac{zN}{2}[\theta E_{AA} + 2\theta(1-\theta)A] + NkT[\theta \ln \theta + (1-\theta)\ln(1-\theta)]$$

where $\theta = x/2 = N_A/N$.

The chemical potential of this gas is

$$\mu = \partial F/\partial N_A = N^{-1}\partial F/\partial \theta$$

the derivative with respect to N_A being taken for a fixed value of N, so

$$\mu(\theta) = \frac{z}{2}[E_{AA} + 2A - 4\theta A] + E_A + kT[\ln \theta - \ln(1-\theta)]$$

$$= E_A + \frac{z}{2}E_{AA} + zA(1-2\theta) + kT \ln \frac{\theta}{1-\theta}$$

As θ increases from 0 to 1, the logarithm increases monotonically from $-\infty$ to $+\infty$, with a least slope of 4 at $\theta=\frac{1}{2}$. If A is positive, then for temperatures below $T_S=zA/2k$ the graph of μ against θ will reverse its slope for some range of θ. In fact, $\partial\mu/\partial\theta$ vanishes at $\theta=\frac{1}{2}\pm\frac{1}{2}(1-T/T_S)^{1/2}$. The corresponding range of μ extends a distance $zA\sqrt{1-T/T_S}-kT\ln\left[(1+\sqrt{1-T/T_S})/(1-\sqrt{1-T/T_S})\right]$ above and below the value $\frac{1}{2}zE_{AA}+E_A$.

To an arbitrarily chosen value of μ within this range, then, correspond three distinct values of θ. The outer pair of these, for both of which $\partial\mu/\partial\theta$ is positive, correspond to thermodynamically stable conditions.

To see this clearly, let us consider the exchange of molecules between the lattice gas (for example, on an adsorbing surface) and a reservoir (for example, of vapour) which fixes the chemical potential. At a surface concentration θ, at which $\partial\mu/\partial\theta$ is positive, the adsorption of more molecules will raise the value of μ. Now matter tends to move from higher to lower μ, so this fluctuation from equilibrium will be restored by re-evaporation of the excess molecules.

At the intermediate solution of $\mu(\theta) = \mu(\text{reservoir})$, on the other hand, $\partial\mu/\partial\theta$ being negative, further adsorption leads to still further adsorption and θ will run up irreversibly to the upper of the stable solutions. Similarly, a downward fluctuation will run right away to the lower stable solution.

Thus at sufficiently low temperatures, for a given value of μ in the appropriate range, the disordered lattice gas may exist in two forms, one of relatively high and the other of low concentration.

These two forms are evidently capable of existing in equilibrium with each other. We have thus an analogy with the phenomenon of condensation of vapour to liquid, the limiting temperature T_S appearing as the analogue of the critical temperature for condensation.

A completely disordered solid solution can be treated in almost exactly the same way, with the precaution that μ is to be calculated recognizing that if N_A or N_B is increased N likewise increases: for example $\mu_A=\partial F/\partial N_A$ for fixed N_B, not for fixed N.

Problem: Take

$$F = \frac{zN}{2}\left[\theta E_{AA}+(1-\theta)E_{BB}+2\theta(1-\theta)A\right]$$
$$+NkT[\theta\ln\theta+(1-\theta)\ln(1-\theta)]$$

calculate μ_A and μ_B, and find the condition that $\partial\mu_A/\partial\theta = 0$, for real values of θ in $0<\theta<1$.

The condition for two different concentrations to equilibrate is again expressed by a non-algebraic equation which becomes very complicated when local ordering and thermal motion are also taken into account. However, there is a very simple expression of the condition in terms of the graph of G/N against θ. This is quite independent of the model considered, involving only classical thermodynamics. The Gibbs free energy G, which we have now introduced, differs from the Helmholtz free energy F only by the addition of PV, which is negligible in condensed systems for pressures near atmospheric.

Suppose that $G = Ng(\theta)$ is known for given T, P. The chemical potentials are defined by $\mu_A = \partial G/\partial N_A$, $\mu_B = \partial G/\partial N_B$ so that for any small variation of composition

$$dG = \mu_A \, dN_A + \mu_B \, dN_B$$

Since the μ depend on θ and not N, except for very small N, we have then

$$G = \mu_A N_A + \mu_B N_B$$

so necessarily

$$dG = \mu_A \, dN_A + \mu_B \, dN_B + N_A \, d\mu_A + N_B \, d\mu_B$$

and we must have the constraint

$$N_A \, d\mu_A + N_B \, d\mu_B = 0$$

In particular

$$\theta \frac{\partial \mu_A}{\partial \theta} + (1-\theta) \frac{\partial \mu_B}{\partial \theta} = 0$$

Now

$$G = N[\theta \mu_A + (1-\theta)\mu_B]$$

i.e.

$$g = \theta \mu_A + (1-\theta)\mu_B$$

and

$$\frac{\partial g}{\partial \theta} = \mu_A - \mu_B + \theta \frac{\partial \mu_A}{\partial \theta} + (1-\theta) \frac{\partial \mu_B}{\partial \theta}$$

$$= \mu_A - \mu_B$$

Thus at any particular value of θ,

$$g = \mu_B + \theta \frac{\partial g}{\partial \theta}$$

The condition that solutions at the same temperature and pressure, but different concentrations θ_1 and θ_2, should equilibrate, is

$$\mu_A(1) = \mu_A(2) \quad \text{and} \quad \mu_B(1) = \mu_B(2)$$

It follows at once that

$$\frac{\partial g}{\partial \theta}(1) = \frac{\partial g}{\partial \theta}(2)$$

that is, that the slope of the graph of g against θ is the same at θ_1 and θ_2. We call its value S.

Then

$$g(1) = \mu_B(1) + S\theta_1$$
$$g(2) = \mu_B(2) + S\theta_2$$

but $\mu_B(1) = \mu_B(2)$, so

$$g(2) - g(1) = S(\theta_2 - \theta_1)$$

that is, the line drawn through $g(1)$ with slope S (tangential to the curve, then) passes through $g(2)$.

Only those solutions can be in mutual equilibrium, then, whose representative points on this diagram (Fig. 8) are the points of contact of common tangents to the curve of $g(\theta)$.

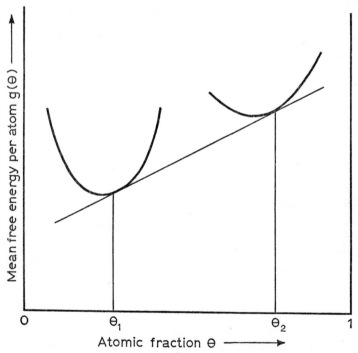

Fig. 8 Construction to find the compositions at which two phases in a two-component system will equilibrate at given temperature

The argument applies even if the equilibrating solutions differ in structure, so that $g(\theta)$ is continuous only in discrete sections.

Lattice models of the liquid state[1]

The fact that critical phenomena on surfaces and in solid solution can be represented in terms of the lattice gas makes it tempting to construct some similar model of the liquid state. In this state, however, there is no immediate guide to the choice of lattice, since no regular geometrical structure survives melting.

The fundamental property which limits the mesh of the lattice in the method we have been using is that one lattice point may be occupied by only one molecule: immediately neighbouring lattice points may be occupied at the same time. If we do not wish to embark on a new calculation of configuration statistics, then, the separation of nearest neighbour lattice points must not be less than a molecular diameter.

There is already a fair difference between a molecular diameter estimated from the density of the crystal near absolute zero and the density near the melting point. Typical materials expand by about 10% in volume over this range, and by about another 10% on melting. In any event, the maximum reasonable density of lattice points will correspond to close packing at a separation equal to the intermolecular distance at zero temperature.

In the original version of Lennard-Jones and Devonshire, the number of lattice points was taken equal to the number of molecules, and each molecule was regarded as moving in a cell of volume equal to the average volume per molecule. The potential field in which it moved was estimated by supposing the cells to be in close-packing, and setting each neighbouring molecule at the centre of its cell—as in the Einstein model of a close-packed crystal.

Problem: Assume cubic close-packing, and a Lennard-Jones potential such as $\phi(r) = ar^{-12} - br^{-6}$, for the interaction of two molecules. At what interatomic distance does the potential energy of a molecule at the centre of its cell change character from a minimum to a maximum?

Hint: Since the only ellipsoid of cubic symmetry is a sphere, you

---

[1] We shall follow certain developments of a method originally due to J. E. Lennard-Jones and A. F. Devonshire (*Proc. Roy. Soc.* **A170**, p. 464, 1939, and earlier) which are summarized and extended by J. S. Rowlinson and C. F. Curtiss (*J. Chem. Phys.* **19**, p. 1519, 1951).

need only consider displacements along a symmetry axis chosen for your convenience.

At liquid densities the potential field near the centre of the cell is nearly a harmonic oscillator potential, and the model is identical with the Einstein picture of a crystal. At much lower densities, each molecule is practically uninfluenced by its neighbours, and its partition function is nearly that for perfectly free motion through the volume of its cell.

However, there is a problem about the entropy. In discussing the Einstein crystal model previously, we had no need to consider the identity of molecules, because what is located at each lattice point is not a particular molecule but a state of excitation. Alternatively, if we consider the molecules labelled there are $N!$ configurations for N distinct molecules on N sites, and this factor is just cancelled by the $N!$ permutations of the molecules among themselves.

When a system is expanded, in the cell model, the same consideration leads us to write for the partition function of N non-interacting molecules in total volume V the expression

$$\left(\frac{V}{N\Lambda^3}\right)^N$$

which is much less than the true value which we have previously shown to be

$$\frac{1}{N!}\left(\frac{V}{\Lambda^3}\right)^N$$

The error is a factor of e^{-N}, which implies an underestimate of the entropy by just k per molecule.

This extra entropy, which any correct theory must build in, in suitable stages, along the transformation from crystal to vapour, is often called the communal entropy, and is extensively discussed in the earlier literature. Eyring suggested that while the simple cell model failed to account for melting, and therefore could not be right for both crystal and liquid, the cell model with the communal entropy arbitrarily added might be a good model for the liquid. The fact that the entropies of melting of several simple liquids are between k and $2k$ per molecule does make this seem reasonable.

Lennard-Jones and Devonshire constructed a model for the melting of a crystal which brought in an entropy of fusion corresponding to disorder of the molecules over a larger number of sites.

To have a well-defined model, they considered the 'octahedral' interstitial sites in a face-centred cubic crystal to be added as a β-class to the α or normal sites. These interstitial sites relate to the normal sites exactly as the sodium ion positions in rock-salt relate to the chlorine ion positions, and are equal in number to them.

This system can be treated to a good approximation by the quasi-chemical method, and gives a good value for the entropy change and the change of volume on melting if the ordering energy is chosen so as to give the correct melting point. The distribution of molecules is nearly completely randomized above the melting point, and the corresponding change, $k \ln 2$, of configurational entropy accounts for about half the entropy of fusion.

A crystal at finite temperature already has some of its regular lattice sites unoccupied. In many substances the equilibrium number of interstitial sites occupied is much less than the number of regular sites vacant, so that the total number of regular sites, both occupied and vacant, increases with rising temperature. One should expect correspondingly to have vacant cells in the liquid model.

Since, however, the volume expansion from zero temperature through the melting point is only of the order of 20%, the number of cells in the liquid near the melting point can only be about 20% more than the number of molecules, rather than 100% more as Lennard-Jones and Devonshire require. These authors suggest that many vacant cells will shrink in the same sort of way that thin cracks in a crystal collapse, their walls drawing together, but it is far from clear that empty cells can shrink without disappearing.

The comparative success of their model in describing liquid properties suggests indeed that the number of distinct configurations of a liquid near its melting point may be equivalent to the number of arrangements of the molecules on a lattice with twice their number of sites.

The question immediately arises whether distinct irregular configurations of the liquid can actually be mapped as distinct configurations on a regular lattice of sufficiently many points; in particular, if it can be done in such a way that nearest neighbours remain nearest neighbours in every instance. The answer to the particular question is almost certainly no, for the reason that the random structure probably produces such things as five-membered rings in more profusion than any crystalline structure could do.

The more general question leads to an exploration of statistical geometry, which is at present a largely experimental science. Studies of random packings made by J. D. Bernal and others reveal a number of interesting features which are best described in terms of a certain 'natural' choice of cells.

At any instant, there is a region surrounding each molecule which belongs to that molecule, in the sense that points in the region are nearer to the centre of gravity of the given molecule than to that of any other molecule. This region is a polyhedron known as the Voronoi polyhedron, and is obtained by the following construction. We join the centre of the given molecule to the centre of its nearest neighbour and construct the plane which is the perpendicular bisector of that straight line. The operation is repeated for each of the less near neighbours in turn, until a closed polyhedron is formed. It may still be possible to cut off some of its corners by continuing the construction, so we go on until we reach a neighbour whose distance from the original centre is more than twice the distance from that centre of the most distant point in the smallest closed polyhedron, enclosing the centre, formed by the planes already drawn. The set of Voronoi polyhedra fills the whole space available to the system.

If then the Voronoi polyhedra are taken as the cells, in the sense of the statistical model, there are by definition no empty cells, and we lose the contribution to the configurational entropy from random distribution over more cells than molecules. The counterbalancing feature is the distribution of types of Voronoi polyhedra. This distribution cannot be entirely random, though D. H. Everett has shown that if one groups the polyhedra simply according to the number of faces, and estimates the entropy of random mixing of the groups of polyhedra in the proportions found by Bernal's model experiment, a fair value of the liquid entropy near the melting point is reproduced.

Bernal and Finney, on the other hand, have shown that the internal energy computed directly from the model distribution of bond lengths gives a very good value for the heat of fusion, so the model is by this (rather weak) test as random as the real liquid. Further development in this direction depends very much at present on the use of electronic computers to simulate model experiments.

Returning now to the problem of constructing a cell model, with vacant cells, for a liquid or dense gas, we should like to choose a cell size such that configurations with more than one molecule per cell are unlikely, while interactions between molecules in nearest-neighbour cells alone need to be considered in the statistics. These two requirements are mutually compatible only for short-range intermolecular forces. A helpful test of consistency will be to carry through the calculation for an arbitrarily chosen cell volume and minimize the resulting free energy with respect to that cell volume as a variable. If the 'best' cell volume emerging from this satisfies the first two requirements, the method is at least not self-contradictory.

If then we have N_A molecules distributed over N cells, we have an Ising lattice gas, whose partition function in the quasi-chemical approximation is the product of a translation factor, which we write as $(v_f/\Lambda^3)^{N_A}$ where v_f is a free volume, and a configuration factor $\exp(-F_c/kT)$. This free energy F_c will be of the form calculated previously for a disordered lattice gas (see p. 119) only if (v_f/Λ^3) for each cell depends on the occupation of neighbouring cells in a very restricted way. As will be seen, some care is then needed in relating v_f to β.

At high densities, several cells around any given one will be occupied on average, and the average potential field, due to its neighbours, which each molecule experiences in its own cell will be nearly that of a spherical harmonic oscillator. It will then be natural to set

$$v_f/\Lambda^3 = (kT/h\nu)^3$$

where ν depends on the density and (slightly) on the selected cell volume. In the limit of very high density, $N \doteq N_A$ and the partition function is

$$\left(\frac{kT}{h\nu}\right)^{3N_A} \exp\left(-\frac{zN_A}{2}\frac{E_{AA}}{kT}\right)$$

where E_{AA}, of course, also depends on density.

At very low densities, neighbour cells are on average empty and v_f is just the volume of the cell, V/N. Then the partition function is

$$\frac{N!}{N_A!(N-N_A)!}\left(\frac{V}{N\Lambda^3}\right)^{N_A} \doteq \frac{1}{N_A!}\left(\frac{V}{\Lambda^3}\right)^{N_A}$$

for $N \gg N_A$.

This method, then, brings in the communal entropy smoothly as density decreases. In the ideal gas limit, it will give the correct partition function independently of the size chosen for the cell, provided only that the cell size does not go to infinity with V, for a given value of N_A.[1]

At intermediate densities, different molecules have different sets of neighbours, and we must consider how the free volume in one cell

---

[1] This is precisely what goes wrong in the original method of Lennard-Jones and Devonshire. The cells, unlike the Voronoi polyhedra, have no physical status: they are merely aids to calculation, and may be chosen of any size. But, if we choose cells so large that at a given density we are likely to find more than one molecule in one cell, the correspondence with the two-state Ising model vanishes and all the statistics must be recalculated. This is very clearly brought out by J. G. Kirkwood (*J. Chem. Phys.* **18**, p. 380, 1950).

depends on the occupation of the neighbour cells. Our guide in this is the requirement that minimizing the constrained free energy for given bond numbers, with respect to the bond numbers, must lead to the form of partition function already quoted.

This can only happen if the v_f factor for a given occupied cell depends on the number $z(1-w)$ of occupied neighbours in just the same way as the corresponding bond-energy factor $\exp\left[-\frac{1}{2}z(1-w)\right.$ $\left.\times E_{AA}/kT\right]$. This is guaranteed if $\ln v_f = wa_1 + (1-w)a_0$, a linear dependence of $\ln v_f$ on w. Set $a_{1,0} = \ln j_{1,0}$

One can now either force the expression to be correct at very high or very low densities, by choosing $j_1 = v_f(1)$, $j_0 = v_f(0)$, or regard j_0 and j_1 as parameters to be adjusted so as to get v_f right (by minimizing the free energy) at the actual density under inspection.

Using the simpler approach, we see that $v_f(1)$ is the free volume in a cell whose neighbours are all empty, so is just the volume of the cell: $v_f(0)/\Lambda^3$, on the other hand, is the partition function of the single particle in a cell all of whose neighbours are occupied. At liquid densities near the melting point, this will be near enough $(kT/hv)^3$.

Problem: How will v depend on N at fixed density, for the Lennard-Jones potential? For $w \neq 0$ or 1, the potential field is generally asymmetric. Consider the isotropic approximation in which each neighbour cell is occupied by $(1-w)$ of a molecule.

We have now associated with each molecule with $z(1-w)$ neighbours a factor in the partition function

$$\exp\left[-\frac{z(1-w)E_{AA}}{2kT}\right] j_0^{(1-w)} j_1^w$$

$$= j_0 \exp\left(-\frac{zE_{AA}}{2kT}\right) \exp\left\{\frac{zw}{2kT}\left[E_{AA} + \frac{2kT}{z}\ln\left(\frac{j_1}{j_0}\right)\right]\right\}$$

The total partition function is then

$$\frac{N!}{N_A!(N-N_A)!} j_0^{N_A} \exp\left(-\frac{zN_A E_{AA}}{2kT}\right)$$

$$\times \left[\frac{\beta-1+2\theta}{\theta(\beta+1)}\right]^{\frac{1}{2}zN_A} \left[\frac{\beta+1-2\theta}{(1-\theta)(\beta+1)}\right]^{\frac{1}{2}z(N-N_A)}$$

where β is now given by

$$\beta^2 = 1 + 4\theta(1-\theta)[(j_1/j_0)^{-2/z} e^{-E_{AA}/kT} - 1]$$

corresponding to an increase of E_{AA} by $(2kT/z)\ln(j_1/j_0)$.

It turns out that the developments of this model give an unsatisfactory account of the critical region. It is suspected, though hardly yet proved, that this is due to underestimate of the communal entropy at intermediate densities.

Although the statistical mechanics of liquids cannot be further developed here, considerable progress has been made in the last twenty years both by numerical calculation with large high-speed computers and by analytical calculation with more powerful mathematical methods. There are still very few exact results known for three-dimensional systems, but the exact theorems which are known for systems in one and two dimensions provide stringent tests for the approximation schemes which are suggested for the treatment of liquids in three dimensions.

J. A. Barker has developed an approximate theory of liquids, which is probably a nearly exact theory of liquid crystals, based on the exact partition function for a one-dimensional gas of interacting particles.[1]

[1] A clear discussion is given in his book, *Lattice theories of the liquid state* (Pergamon, 1963).

9

LONG-RANGE FORCES

Long-range interactions—gravity and Coulomb forces

If the interactions between particles fall off sufficiently rapidly with distance, a sensible first approximation is obtained by considering only the interaction of each particle with the small group of its nearest neighbours—those particles whose Voronoi polyhedra have a face in common with that of the central particle. This is by no means true of interactions which fall off more slowly. The inverse square law of force gives rise to several interesting problems of this nature.

Gravitational repulsion is unknown, and it is easy to see that in consequence the chemical potential of a substance at given concentration cannot be independent of the total mass of it present.

The gravitational potential at the surface of a sphere of mass m and radius r is

$$-Gmr^{-1}$$

where G is the gravitational constant, so the gain in energy of an increment dm added to it is

$$-Gmr^{-1}\,dm$$

If moreover Gmr^{-2} is so small that the addition distorts neither m nor dm (distortion due to weight and reaction), this energy gain is the whole gravitational contribution to the chemical potential per unit mass, which is then

$$-Gmr^{-1}$$

or, if the sphere is of uniform density ρ

$$-4\pi\rho Gr^2/3$$

Since G is exceedingly small compared with the constants of the Van der Waals and valence forces, the gravitational potential per molecule is comparable to kT, at terrestrial surface temperatures, only for bodies of planetary mass. The internal pressures in planets, and still more in stars, are so great that the PV term in the Gibbs free energy is not merely considerable but sometimes dominant in determining the thermal behaviour.

The general relation of pressure to density, in a spherical gravitating body in hydrostatic equilibrium, is easy to find, for it simply states that the weight of an element of the body is balanced by the difference in pressure on its horizontal faces. The weight is determined by the mass of the element and the mass of that part of the body which lies nearer to the centre. Thus

$$\frac{\mathrm{d}p}{\mathrm{d}r} = -\frac{\rho G}{r^2} \int_0^r 4\pi r^2 \rho \, \mathrm{d}r$$

where pressure p and density ρ are some functions of r. Obviously $\mathrm{d}p/\mathrm{d}r=0$ at $r=0$.

For some purposes it is more transparent to rearrange and differentiate this relation, giving

$$\frac{1}{r^2} \cdot \frac{\mathrm{d}}{\mathrm{d}r} \left(\frac{r^2}{\rho} \cdot \frac{\mathrm{d}p}{\mathrm{d}r} \right) = -4\pi G\rho$$

The condition $\mathrm{d}p/\mathrm{d}r=0$ at $r=0$, of which we lose track on differentiating, must now be explicitly restated.

Further progress depends on finding another usable relation between p and ρ. This will be amply supplied by the equation of state if we know the temperature as a function of r. The temperature depends in general on the mechanisms of heat generation and heat escape—for example, a planet could well have a large isothermal core surrounded by a layer of radioactive rocks whose energy output supplied the whole of the heat flow to the external surface—and these depend in turn on, at least, the local temperature and density, leading to a rather nasty group of interlocking relations.[1]

As a short-cut we may postulate a convenient algebraic relation between p and ρ, perhaps something like an adiabatic equation of state. The true adiabatic relation would have one advantage, that in a region free of energy sources this temperature distribution would be undisturbed by radial currents. Matter flowing slowly in or out would by adiabatic compression or expansion adjust to the temperature

[1] An excellent but not very elementary discussion of such questions is given in S. Chandrasekhar's *Introduction to the Study of Stellar Structure*.

appropriate to its level. Such currents would not then disturb the hydrostatic equilibrium by upsetting the pressure-density relation which that equilibrium requires.

Trial of $p = P\rho^\gamma$ leads to

$$\frac{1}{r^2} \frac{d}{dr} \left(r^2 \rho^{\gamma-2} \frac{d\rho}{dr} \right) = -\frac{4\pi G}{\gamma P} \rho$$

with $dp/dr = 0$ at $r = 0$. The arbitrary choice of $\gamma = 2$ leads to the simple result

$$\rho = Ar^{-1} \sin kr$$

where $k^2 = 2\pi G/\rho$.

It would evidently be wise to keep the surface of our body inside R_0, where $kR_0 = \pi$. Setting the surface at R_0, with $\rho = p = 0$ at all points outside, meets the conditions so far imposed and leaves A, and so the total mass, completely unspecified. We have therefore a set of equilibrium bodies all of the same radius and of all conceivable masses.

One might conclude that the proposed equation, at least with $\gamma = 2$, was thus shown to be inapplicable.

Problem: Discuss the use of $p = P(\rho^2 - \rho_0^2)$.

Certainly lower values of γ are more plausible. However, they lead to almost equally remarkable conclusions. For example, the large class of dense stars known as the white dwarves is believed to be cold in the sense that the equation of state is essentially independent of the temperature.

R. H. Fowler first suggested that the density in the interior of these stars is so high that the extended structure of electron shells, which characterizes atoms in the normal states of matter, is wholly broken down. This dense matter consists of atomic nuclei floating in a Fermi gas of essentially free electrons. It is effectively cold because the Fermi energy is much larger than kT in the star.

Problem: A typical white dwarf might have a mass of 10^{30} kg, a radius of 10^7 m and a surface temperature of 10^4 K. What would the internal temperature T_i have to be if kT_i were to be equal to the Fermi energy of electrons in cold matter at the average density of this star? (Assume that the atomic nuclei present contain on average equal numbers of protons and neutrons.)

The pressure of a cold electron gas is easily seen (e.g. from $\xi_0 \propto n^{2/3}$)

to be proportional to the 5/3 power of the density, so long as the Fermi energy is much less than the rest energy of an electron. In the extreme relativistic limit all particles look like photons, with energy just equal to the size of the momentum multiplied by the speed of light; ξ_0 becomes proportional to $n^{1/3}$ and γ drops to 4/3.

Even with $\gamma = 5/3$, it turns out that the radius of a white dwarf should decrease with increasing mass. The cold plasma is too compressible to support itself against its own weight, when a sufficient mass is present. Landau showed as early as 1932 (see, for example, Chandrasekhar's book already quoted) that the radius of the white dwarf should go to zero at a mass not very much larger than that of the sun—and much less than the mass of many known normal stars. A point particle of solar mass would indeed be an interesting object.

At least one phase change must intervene as the density increases. The free neutron moving in ordinary matter is a radioactive particle, decaying into a proton, an electron and an antineutrino with a lifetime of about 12 minutes.

$$n \to p + e + \bar{\nu}$$

The energy release in the reaction is 780 keV.

If the neutron moves in a Fermi sea of electrons of depth greater than 780 keV (well over the electron rest energy, as it happens) this decay is inhibited, for there is not enough energy to raise the product electron to the Fermi surface. In fact, protons and electrons now revert to neutrons and neutrinos by the reaction

$$p + e \to n + \nu$$

Problem: At what numerical density of electrons is the Fermi energy equal to 780 keV? The distribution in momentum is the same as in the non-relativistic case, but we must take the total energy E of each electron (Fermi energy plus rest energy of the electron) as given in terms of the momentum p and rest-mass m_0 by the general relation

$$E^2 = p^2 c^2 + m_0^2 c^4$$

where c is the speed of light.

At very high density, then, the stable state of matter consists of a Fermi sea of neutrons, with just enough electrons—and the corresponding protons—to inhibit the neutron β-decay. This is still a Fermi fluid, and the maximum mass of a neutron star is still little more than that of the sun. Moreover, there is no experimental evidence for the existence of neutron stars, other than the appearance, in the pulsating radio stars, of bodies which are both too energetic and too small to be white dwarfs of the more usual sort.

The problem of what possible fate awaits massive stars when their reserves of thermonuclear fuel run out must be left to the speculations of the astrophysicists. The cold 'plasma', well established as the state of matter in the white dwarfs, leads our attention to the plasma state at lower concentrations, where the charged particles are non-degenerate at accessible temperatures.

Debye–Hückel theory of electrolytes

Much of both technical chemistry and biochemistry is concerned with the behaviour in water of substances which are seen, e.g. from electrolytic phenomena, to dissociate as they dissolve into electrically charged particles. The overall electrical neutrality of the solution avoids the size effects which are quite inevitable in gravitation, and the thermodynamic potentials depend only on the concentrations, the pressure and the temperature.

A solution containing only two sorts of ion might be described as a three-component lattice gas. In view of the long-range interactions, the count of configurations of approximately equal energy can not be handled by the methods of the last chapter, and we start with a different set of approximations, emphasizing first of all the electro-static interaction energy.

This electrostatic interaction separates into two parts, interaction of ions with solvent, and of ions with ions. Good ionizing solvents, in which a salt like sodium chloride will dissolve freely as separate sodium and chlorine ions rather than as the diatomic sodium chloride molecule, must respond to the ionic charges so as to lower their free energy in solution. Solvents such as water and ammonia have large molecular dipole moments and correspondingly large dielectric constants.

The large dielectric constant not only lowers the energy of solution of a given ion, but reduces the effective interaction of ions with each other. There is a complication because the electric field close to an ion is so strong that dielectric saturation occurs. For this reason among others, the elementary treatment to be described, following the early work of Debye and Hückel, is applicable only to very dilute solutions.

Ionic atmosphere near a fixed charge

We consider first the electric field and ionic concentrations in equili-brium in the neighbourhood of a fixed point charge Q, supposing that the ions have charges z_1q and z_2q, where q is the charge of a proton, and the medium has dielectric constant ϵ. Let the numerical concentrations of the ions at distance r from Q be $n_1(r)$ and $n_2(r)$ respectively.

The charge within a sphere of radius R centred on Q is evidently

$$Q + q \int_0^R (z_1 n_1 + z_2 n_2) 4\pi r^2 \, dr = 4\pi R^2 \, \mathscr{D}(R) \tag{A}$$

where $\mathscr{D}$ is the radial electric displacement. The electric intensity $E = \mathscr{D}/\epsilon$, and the electric potential at R with respect to a zero at infinite distance is

$$\phi(R) = \int_0^\infty E(r) \, dr$$

so

$$\mathscr{D}(R) = -\epsilon \, d\phi/dR$$

Differentiating equation (A) with respect to R gives then

$$-\epsilon \frac{d}{dR} \left(R^2 \frac{d\phi}{dR} \right) = qR^2(z_1 n_1 + z_2 n_2)$$

The concentrations n_1 and n_2 depend on ϕ, being in fact determined by the constancy of the chemical potentials μ_1 and μ_2 of the ions throughout the system. The potential μ_1, for example, contains a term $z_1 q \phi$. If we assume that it contains no other terms dependent on ϕ or E we are ignoring various effects of polarization or electrostriction, which can be comparable with the original term only for particular systems and very close to the central charge.

In addition, we make the strongest simplifying assumption about the rest of the μ, namely, that apart from the electrostatic interaction the ions move as if perfectly independent of each other. Then we may write

$$n_1 = N_1 \, e^{-\beta z_1 q \phi}, \qquad n_2 = N_2 \, e^{-\beta z_2 q \phi}$$

where $z_1 N_1 + z_2 N_2 = 0$ expresses the electrical neutrality of the solution far from the perturbing charge Q.

It should be noted that this takes only partial account of the mutual action of the ions, precisely because of the assumption that both sorts of ions see the same potential ϕ. The charge pair, Q with z_1q at distance r, has a different equilibrium atmosphere from Q with z_2q at distance r. To pursue this point leads to substantial improvement in the theory at the cost of substantial mathematical exertion.

We again take the primrose path of linearization, with the additional assumption that $\beta zq\phi$ is in each case much less than unity, so that

$$n_1 = N_1(1 - \beta z_1 q\phi), \qquad n_2 = N_2(1 - \beta z_2 q\phi)$$

$$\frac{1}{R^2}\frac{d}{dR}\left(R^2\frac{d\phi}{dR}\right) = \phi\frac{q^2\beta}{\epsilon}(N_1 z_1^2 + N_2 z_2^2)$$

The solution of this last equation which goes to zero as R goes to infinity is $\phi = f \exp(-R/D)/R$, where D, which is called the Debye length, is given by

$$D^2 = \frac{\epsilon kT}{q^2(N_1 z_1^2 + N_2 z_2^2)}$$

The decaying exponential expresses the screening of the Coulomb force by the ionic atmosphere. If we set the total ionic concentration $N_1 + N_2 = N$, then for given z_1, z_2

$$D \propto (\epsilon T/N)^{1/2}$$

The mean separation of neighbouring ions is

$$L \sim N^{-1/3}$$

so for sufficiently dilute solutions we always have $D \gg L$. In this case there are many ions within a Debye length from any given point, and the discussion in terms of a smoothly varying average potential is likely to be justified.

Problem: What order of concentration would give $D = L$ for monovalent ions in water at room temperature?

The charge Q does not affect the form of the screened potential. It does of course determine the amplitude f, for the electric displacement at some sufficiently small R must be $Q/4\pi R^2$, provided we can find a sphere which contains all of Q and is never entered by other charges. If also the screened Coulomb potential is valid down to this surface, say of radius b, we have outside b

$$E = -\frac{d\phi}{dR} = \frac{f e^{-R/D}}{R}\left(\frac{1}{D} + \frac{1}{R}\right)$$

so

$$\mathscr{D}(b) = \frac{\epsilon f e^{-b/D}}{b}\left(\frac{1}{D} + \frac{1}{b}\right)$$

$$= \frac{Q}{4\pi b^2}$$

i.e.

$$f = \frac{Q \, e^{b/D} \, D}{4\pi\epsilon(b+D)}$$

Then

$$\phi(R) = \frac{Q}{4\pi\epsilon} \cdot \frac{D}{R(b+D)} \, e^{(b-R)/D}$$

The part of this due to the presence of Q itself and the solvent is $Q/4\pi\epsilon R$, so the contribution from the ionic atmosphere is

$$\frac{Q}{4\pi\epsilon R} \left[\frac{D}{b+D} \, e^{(b-R)/D} - 1 \right]$$

In particular, the potential at (and inside) b, due to the surrounding ions is $-Q/[4\pi\epsilon(b+D)]$, which is hardly dependent on b for $b \ll D$.

Problem: There is a net space-charge round Q. Show that the total charge of the ionic atmosphere, with the assumptions made above, is $-Q$.

The interesting application of these results is naturally the situation where the charge Q is itself an ion of radius b and charge zq. The self-energy of such an ion in air is of the order of $(zq)^2/8\pi b\epsilon_0$, being exactly this if the charge is uniformly spread on the surface of a sphere of radius b. The corresponding self-energy in the dielectric is simply obtained by replacing the dielectric constant of the vacuum by that of the medium, so the self-energy drops, when the ion passes into solution, by the amount

$$\frac{1}{8\pi b} (zq)^2 \left(\frac{1}{\epsilon_0} - \frac{1}{\epsilon} \right)$$

The electrostatic binding energy between two ions in a diatomic molecule in vacuum will be

$$\frac{z_1 z_2 q^2}{4\pi(b_1+b_2)\epsilon_0}$$

so there is no difficulty in regaining all of this on dissolving the separate ions in a medium with high ϵ.

For each ion, there is a large term in its free energy

$$\frac{1}{8\pi b} (zq)^2 \left(\frac{1}{\epsilon} - \frac{1}{\epsilon_0} \right)$$

independent of concentration and dependent on temperature only through the temperature dependence of the dielectric constant. We proceed with the identification of the concentration-dependent term.

Reversible charging and electrical free energy

The electrical potential across a condenser of capacitance C, at charge Q, is $V = Q/C$. Addition of an element of charge dQ involves work $V\,dQ = Q\,dQ/C$, so if C is constant through the charging process, the stored energy is $Q^2/2C$ or $\frac{1}{2}CV^2$.

C is the product of a geometrical factor f and the dielectric constant of the insulator, ϵ. For a conducting sphere of radius b, $C = 4\pi b\epsilon$. Since ϵ varies with temperature, rapid charging produces a change in temperature of the dielectric. This change is analogous to the heating of a gas in reversible adiabatic compression, and is quite independent of any dissipative process which may occur.

If the condenser is thermally connected to a thermostat, and charging is so slow that the dielectric remains at constant temperature, a finite heat transfer accompanies the isothermal charging. The capacitance C remains constant, so the electrical work done is $Q^2/2C$, which is evidently stored as free energy in the dielectric.

The recipe for identifying the electrical free energy associated with a charge distribution is, then, to build up the charge reversibly from zero under isothermal conditions and evaluate the work done in the process.

In an ionic solution there are two such imagined processes of dominant interest, leading respectively to the chemical potential and the total free energy.

In the first process, due to Güntelberg, we imagine all ions but one to be already present and bearing their full charge, so that D is fixed at a constant value. The ion of particular interest has instead of charge zq the charge $zq\xi$ where ξ is to be slowly increased from 0 to 1. So far as electrical interactions are concerned, this gives a mechanism for introducing an ion reversibly, without worrying about boundary effects. The charging parameter is an imaginary device, but violates only the law of conservation of charge, which is not part of thermodynamics: in fact, if we switch on simultaneously a small set of far separated ions of zero resultant charge, only the law of quantization of charge is infringed.

At a given value of ξ, the potential at the ion's surface due to its own charge is $zq\xi/4\pi b\epsilon$; the potential due to neighbouring ions is $-zq\xi/[4\pi\epsilon(b+D)]$. Increasing ξ by $d\xi$ adds charge $zq\,d\xi$ at the cost of work

$$\frac{(zq)^2}{4\pi\epsilon}\left(\frac{1}{b} - \frac{1}{b+D}\right)\xi\,d\xi$$

so the total work done in charging to $\xi = 1$ is

$$\frac{(zq)^2}{8\pi\epsilon b} - \frac{(zq)^2}{8\pi\epsilon(b+D)}$$

The first term we have already mentioned as the self-energy. The second term is the ion interaction part of the chemical potential.

Debye applied the charging process to all ions simultaneously, at specified values of N_1, N_2. This gives the electrical part of the Helmholtz free energy. The Debye length is now variable. When each charge is multiplied by ξ, the Debye length becomes D/ξ.

The potential due to neighbouring ions is

$$-\frac{zq}{4\pi\epsilon} \cdot \frac{\xi^2}{b\xi + D}$$

so the work done in the charging process is

$$-\frac{(zq)^2}{4\pi\epsilon} \int_0^1 \frac{\xi^2 \, d\xi}{b\xi + D} = -\frac{(zq)^2}{4\pi\epsilon} \frac{D^2}{b^3} \int_0^{b/D} \frac{x^2 \, dx}{x+1}$$

$$= -\frac{(zq)^2}{4\pi\epsilon D} \left(\frac{1}{3} - \frac{1}{4} \cdot \frac{b}{D} - \cdots \right)$$

The free energy of ionic interaction, then, is in first approximation

$$F_{\text{int}} = -\frac{q^2}{12\pi\epsilon D} (N_1 z_1^2 + N_2 z_2^2)$$

Problem: Verify that this statement is consistent with the chemical potential derived by Güntelberg's approach.

If D is expressed in terms of the N, we obtain

$$F_{\text{int}} = -\frac{q^3}{12\pi\sqrt{kT}} \left(\frac{N_1 z_1^2 + N_2 z_2^2}{\epsilon} \right)^{3/2}$$

quite unlike the $N^{4/3} q^2 / \epsilon$ which gives the order of magnitude of the binding energy of the hydrated crystal—the limit of high concentration and low temperature.

MATHEMATICAL APPENDIX

(1) *Integrals leading to the ζ-function of Riemann*

Various expectation values for the ideal gas of bosons or fermions contain the integral

$$\int_0^\infty \frac{x^m \, dx}{e^x \pm 1} = \int_0^\infty x^m \, e^{-x} \, (1 \mp e^{-x} + e^{-2x} \mp e^{-3x} + \cdots) \, dx$$

The term

$$\int_0^\infty x^m \, e^{-nx} \, dx = n^{-(m+1)} \int_0^\infty y^m \, e^{-y} \, dy$$
$$= m! \, n^{-(m+1)}$$

so

$$\int_0^\infty \frac{x^m \, dx}{e^x \pm 1} = m! \, (1 \mp 2^{-(m+1)} + 3^{-(m+1)} \cdots)$$

The series of positive terms defines Riemann's function $\zeta(m+1)$. The alternating series is

$$\zeta(m+1) - 2[2^{-(m+1)} + 4^{-(m+1)} + \cdots] = (1 - 2^{-m})\zeta(m+1)$$

so

$$\int_0^\infty \frac{x^m \, dx}{e^x \pm 1} = \binom{1 - 2^{-m}}{\text{or } 1} m! \, \zeta(m+1)$$

The ζ-function is fully tabulated in *Tables of Functions* by Jahnke and Emde. A useful set of values is

x	1·5	2	2·5	3	3·5	4
$\zeta(x)$	2·612	1·645	1·341	1·202	1·127	1·082

It is interesting to note that for integral n

$$\zeta(2n) = \tfrac{1}{2}B_n \frac{(2\pi)^{2n}}{(2n)!}$$

where the first few Bernoulli numbers B_n are

n	1	2	3	4
B_n	$\frac{1}{6}$	$\frac{1}{30}$	$\frac{1}{42}$	$\frac{1}{30}$

(2) *A Fermi expectation value*

$$\int_0^\infty \frac{f(x)\,\mathrm{d}x}{\mathrm{e}^{(x-a)}+1} - \int_0^a f(x)\,\mathrm{d}x$$

$$= \int_a^\infty \frac{f(x)\,\mathrm{d}x}{\mathrm{e}^{(x-a)}+1} - \int_0^a f(x)\,\frac{\mathrm{e}^{(x-a)}}{\mathrm{e}^{(x-a)}+1}\,\mathrm{d}x$$

$$= \int_0^\infty \frac{f(x+a)\,\mathrm{d}x}{\mathrm{e}^x+1} - \int_{-a}^0 \frac{f(x+a)\,\mathrm{d}x}{1-\mathrm{e}^{-x}}$$

$$= \int_0^\infty \frac{f(x+a)\,\mathrm{d}x}{\mathrm{e}^x+1} - \int_0^a \frac{f(a-x)\,\mathrm{d}x}{\mathrm{e}^x+1}$$

$$\sim \int_0^\infty \frac{f(a+x)-f(a-x)}{\mathrm{e}^x+1}\,\mathrm{d}x,$$

$$\text{neglecting } \int_a^\infty \frac{f(a-x)\,\mathrm{d}x}{\mathrm{e}^x+1}$$

$$= 2\int_0^\infty \left[xf'(a)+\frac{x^3}{3!}f'''(a)+\cdots \right](\mathrm{e}^x+1)^{-1}\,\mathrm{d}x$$

so

$$\int_0^\infty \frac{f(x)\,\mathrm{d}x}{\mathrm{e}^{(x-a)}+1} \sim \int_0^a f(x)\,\mathrm{d}x+\zeta(2)f'(a)+\tfrac{7}{4}\zeta(4)f'''(a)+\cdots$$

(3) *Debye functions*

The phonons, or quanta of lattice vibration, in a crystal constitute a boson gas with no constraint on number, but with an upper limit on the single-boson energy. In Debye approximation, this upper limit is $k\theta_D$. The finite integrals required for the thermodynamic functions are very well tabulated by Stark and Kortzeborn in University of California Radiation Laboratory Report, no. 17225 (1966).

(4) *Distribution and density functions*

Given a series of events E_r with a quantity x_r associated with each, the set of x_r may be described by the distribution function $D_x(a)$

which is the fraction of the total number of events for which $x_r < a$. Then $0 < D < 1$.

Given many different series from the same class of events, the individual distribution functions crowd towards a limit function as the number of events in each series increases. $D_x(a)$ in this limit is called the probability of $(x < a)$.

$p_x(a) = (d/da)D_x(a)$ is the probability density function for x. In physical measurement, p_x commonly has one single maximum. The p.d.f. is itself often called distribution function, especially by physicists.

The moments of x are the expectation values of x^n for integral n. p_x is often sufficiently characterized by only the first two moments.

$$\bar{x} = \int_{-\infty}^{\infty} xp(x)\, dx$$

$$\overline{x^2} = \int_{-\infty}^{\infty} x^2 p(x)\, dx$$

Note that the mean square deviation from the mean, which is the most convenient measure of the dispersion of x, is given by

$$\overline{(x-\bar{x})^2} = \int_{-\infty}^{\infty} (x-\bar{x})^2 p(x)\, dx$$

$$= \overline{x^2} - 2\bar{x}\cdot\bar{x} + \bar{x}^2$$

$$= \overline{x^2} - \bar{x}^2$$

The normal distribution, which often represents a series of good measurements of a single quantity, has p.d.f.

$$p(x) = \frac{1}{\sqrt{2\pi\sigma^2}}\, e^{-(x-a)^2/2\sigma^2}$$

where $\bar{x} = a$, $\overline{x^2} - \bar{x}^2 = \sigma^2$. The mean and the m.s. deviation, then, suffice to determine the normal distribution function.

(5) Conditional probability

Associate probabilities p_{ij} (probability of E_j and H_i) with joint events constructed from classes E and H.

$$p(H_i \mid E_j) = \frac{p_{ij}}{\sum_{i} p_{ij}}$$

is conditional probability of H_i, given E_j, and

$$p(E_j) = \sum_i p_{ij}$$

is probability of E_j for any H_i at all.

Then

$$p(H_i \mid E_j)p(E_j) = p_{ij} = p(E_j \mid H_i)p(H_i)$$

or

$$\frac{p(H_i \mid E_j)}{p(H_i)} = \frac{p(E_j \mid H_i)}{p(E_j)}$$

This result is profitably used with a rather different interpretation of the symbols.

(6) Likeliness

I regard an event E as having likeliness P when I am prepared to wager P against $(1-P)$, on stakes I can afford to lose, on the occurrence of E (and simultaneously, in the usual terms of a fair wager, to bet $(1-P)$ against P on the non-occurrence of E). If events E_j have known probabilities (in the sense of limiting frequency fractions) p_j, I must for consistency make $P_j = p_j$, and then actual relations among p's must correspond to true relations among P's.

In particular

$$\frac{P(H_i \mid E_j)}{P(H_i)} = \frac{P(E_j \mid H_i)}{P(E_j)} \qquad \text{(Bayes equation)}$$

(7) Verification

H_i are a set of alternative hypotheses about a situation; E_j are alternative events occurring in the situation. The occurrence of a particular E_j lends support to H_i in the sense that the likeliness of H_i, given E_j, is to the *a priori* likeliness of H_i as the likeliness of E_j, given H_i, is to the the likeliness of E_j, irrespective of hypothesis.

Very commonly, H_i is precisely a statement about the P_j (which, if H_i were true, would be a statement about the p_j). Then the right-hand side of Bayes equation is known for each H and E. With luck, $P(H_i)$, which is hard to estimate, is not vastly different for different H_i.

FURTHER READING

No book is likely to be so bad as to contain no useful knowledge. Here are a few really good ones.

Information theory

J. R. Pierce, *Symbols, signals and noise* (Hutchinson, 1962)—a first-class introduction.

A. I. Khinchin, *Mathematical foundations of information theory* (Dover, 1957), and A. Feinstein, *Foundations of information theory* (McGraw-Hill, 1958)—excellent but not very easy mathematical books.

Thermodynamics

M. W. Zemansky, *Heat and thermodynamics* (McGraw-Hill, 1968)—an excellent undergraduate text.

E. A. Guggenheim, *Thermodynamics* (North-Holland, 1957)—covers the whole field of chemical thermodynamics. Use a recent edition.

P. T. Landsberg, *Thermodynamics* (Interscience, 1961)—concerned primarily with the foundations of the subject, and contains a great deal of statistical mechanics.

Statistical mechanics

E. Schrödinger, *Statistical thermodynamics* (Cambridge, 1952)—a little book full of lucid understanding.

J. S. Dugdale, *Entropy and low temperature physics* (Hutchinson, 1966)—particularly interesting on the low-temperature region where thermal behaviour depends strongly on quantum properties.

D. ter Haar, *Elements of thermostatistics* (Holt, Rinehart, Winston, 1966)—follows the great Dutch physicist H. Kramers in a very complete account at advanced undergraduate level.

A. Katz, *Principles of statistical mechanics* (Freeman, 1967)—a good short book based on information theory, not going very far into applications.

R. Kubo, *Statistical mechanics* (North-Holland, 1965)—a good book with a particularly valuable and extensive collection of worked problems.

M. Tribus, *Thermostatistics and thermodynamics* (Van Nostrand, 1961)—a large and very complete book based on the information theory approach due to E. T. Jaynes.

R. H. Fowler, *Statistical mechanics* (Cambridge, 1936) and R. H. Fowler and E. A. Guggenheim, *Statistical thermodynamics* (Cambridge, 1939)—two large standard works which are still very useful.

T. L. Hill, *Statistical mechanics* (McGraw-Hill, 1956) and K. Huang, *Statistical mechanics* (Wiley, 1965)—both excellent modern advanced texts, at post-graduate rather than undergraduate level.

L. D. Landau and E. M. Lifshitz, *Statistical physics* (Pergamon, 1969) —a master-work by the great Russian physicist and his colleague, with the emphasis on physical ideas but using a full range of theoretical techniques.

G. S. Rushbrooke, *Introduction to statistical mechanics* (Oxford University Press, 1949)—an excellent text on traditional lines, rich in chemical applications, very slightly more mathematical than the present book, but extremely clear on many particular points.

R. C. Tolman, *Principles of statistical mechanics* (Oxford, reprinted 1959)—an old book now, but still with the best and clearest account of many points in classical and quantum mechanics as well as in statistical mechanics.

The fundamental paper which establishes the viewpoint developed in this book is by E. T. Jaynes, in *Physical Review* **106**, pp. 620–630, 1957.

INDEX